Robert
7813 NE 14th Street
Vancouver, WA 98664

BOB - THANK-YOU FOR
LENDING US THE BOOK
(AND OUR LITTLE EVINRUDE
THANKS YOU ALSO) OF
SAILBOAT ENGINES - IT
TWAS HELPFULL.

Bryan
(CAPTAIN OF "RECLUSE")
MAY - 1994

Engines for
Sailboats

The yachtsman's guide to
selection, installation,
first aid and maintenance
of sailing craft powerplants

CONRAD
MILLER

Yachting BOOKS
Ziff-Davis Publishing Company

FIRST EDITION

ISBN 0–87165–011–8

Jacket and book design by Victoria Blanchard

This book is dedicated to all Corinthians
who have had to struggle with a cranky auxiliary
and especially to my wife, Marian, and sons Winslow,
John, and Keith, who have sometimes had to
struggle with a cranky author as well.
C.M.

Contents

Preface

This book is aimed at the sailboat skipper who owns or charters a boat having an engine for auxiliary power. The man or woman to whom the book is addressed loves boats and sailing, but looks down upon his sailboat's engine as a necessary evil. He doesn't like the monster; he may even hate it. But if he wants to work in and out of harbors easily, pass through drawbridges without a donnybrook, and get home when the wind fails, alas, he needs that mechanical propulsion.

You are that skipper: You may not love your auxiliary, but have to live with it. It's like an unwanted child, and like the child if you try to understand it and give it reasonable care, the engine will be easier to get along with. Responding to kindness, it may someday run counter to Murphy's Law.* It may perform perfectly when you need it most desperately.

The purpose of this book is to help you give your auxiliary at least minimal care, assisting you in making it run when it's cranky, and convincing you that it is worth at least as much care as the head. What's written here may demonstrate to you that the thing is not quite the beast that you think. If we can't make you love it, perhaps we can, through your deeper understanding, at least help you tolerate its strange ways, and help it through some of its worst days.

We also hope we can bolster your confidence. We'll try to show that the brute is not quite as cantankerous as you might think, and that, without assistance, you can fix ninety percent of its troubles, real or imagined, when the chips are down.

Who knows? Someday after the old grinder has helped you claw to windward off a rocky shore, you might even pat it affectionately on its cylinder head, saying, "Well done, old friend."

*Most boating people are familiar with Murphy's Law, which states: "If anything *can* go wrong it *will.*" And there is also Miller's corollary stating, "The more desperately you need the auxiliary, the more certainly it will not run."

1
The Misunderstood Auxiliary How It's Different

How come sailboat auxiliaries are so cantankerous? Why are they such a nuisance? Who can ever depend on one when he needs it? Why is it that an automobile engine runs month in, month out for thousands of miles giving no trouble, but a sailboat's auxiliary quits when you need it, and is a downright horror. How come?

"How come?" is easy to explain. The way the two engines live and are used is miles apart. Each may start life equally reliable, but after that, the car engine has the best of it: Used every day, it has little time to mold and rust. It is exercised regularly and at least looked at by the guy who wipes the windshield and checks the oil.

How different is the life of the auxiliary! An hour or two per week typifies its running time for the sailing season. Then it lies rusting for months on end, no one as much as casting a glance its way. It is not *use* which makes the auxiliary balky, it's disuse and neglect.

Compared to the automobile, truck, bus, or even to the runabout engine, the sailboat auxiliary is operated in a substantially different manner. What follows here delineates specifically how the auxiliary's environment and application are different. Along with this brief analysis you'll find suggestions which, I hope, will help you minimize the ill effects of the sailboat engine's intermittent life aboard your yacht.

Rust and corrosion attack both the exterior and innards of your auxiliary. Its high-humidity environment—i.e., dew, condensate, salt, and mist—invites oxidation and metal deterioration. This leads to mechanical troubles. Worse, it invites electrical problems because wires and connections go to pot. The result, of course, is hard starting, rough running, and engine failure at embarrassing moments.

1

You can negate some of the foul work done by salt and moisture: Open up the engine compartment as often as possible, giving the damp machine some sun and air. Dry it out as frequently as possible. When you're in the mood, rub it down with a thirsty dry rag or wad of paper towels. Then wipe it all over with an oily rag. Better still, spray it with a mist of CRC Compound or other anti-moisture oil after you've dried it. Doing this a couple of times each sailing season will work wonders in improving the monster's disposition. Remember, too, if the engine is of the gasoline variety with electric ignition, spray the distributor wires with anti-moisture compound. Some damp morning when you want to power out to the starting line, you'll be glad you did.

Short runs generate all kinds of problems for the auxiliary. Often you fire up the mill, run just long enough to push your way out of the marina and get your main hoisted; then you shut her down. The engine's innards have had insufficient time to warm to their work, resulting in conditions which breed later problems.

This fit-and-start running causes internal accumulations of moisture, leading to rust. Such running contaminates the oil, inviting valves and stuck piston rings. Furthermore, this kind of operation can cause moisture to condense in the inlet manifold of the gasoline engine. The moisture generates rust; the rust flakes off, and the first thing you know the engine is a hard starter and frequent staller: Flakes and minute chips of rust have loused up its carburetor.

Your approach to minimizing the ills caused by short runs is obvious, if not always possible. Make long runs. Put the engine to work and keep it grinding away until its water, oil, and metal are good and hot. It's pretty hard to get any gasoline or diesel engine thoroughly warmed in less than 20 minutes. Whenever you start the beast, try to run it under load for at least that length of time.

Partially discharged and dead storage batteries cause more swearing among sailors than all the fouled halyards, tangled spinnakers, and jammed main sheets combined. Your automobile's battery gives far less trouble because it gets well charged every day. To a lesser extent, that applies to the runabout battery. But the battery serving your sailboat's auxiliary seldom gets enough charging time to keep it tip-top. Short, infrequent runs and hard starts are responsible for auxiliary battery problems. Compounding the felony are numerous accessories hung on the electrical system, draining the cells of energy.

Your strategy for helping the engine's starting battery should include several avenues of attack, and we'll expand on the details later in this book: Follow our earlier advice; make your powered runs longer. Have one battery for engine starting only, connecting all electrical accessories to other batteries. Get the alternator or generator charge rate adjusted to a higher than normal value, say 15 volts on a nominal 12-volt system. Where possible, use a dockside charger to keep the cells topped up when the boat is not in use. Take it easy on using battery-energized accessories when the engine is not running, and never connect heavy-demand accessories, such as a refrigerator, to the engine starting battery. (See Chapter XI for more details.)

While the auto engine hums along on even keel over smooth, level roads, the auxiliary is subjected to a topsy-turvy life. Rolled and pitched, yawed and heeled in a most disturbing fashion, it's sometimes laid on beam ends for hours. If it's an outboard, it is tilted up at a crazy angle off the transom while being sprayed with navigable water and possibly drenched with rain. After all this gyrating, do you seriously expect the thing to run?

Of course you expect it to run. But the undulating environment is working against you. Extremes of motion stir up sediment in the fuel tank, upset the carburetor, and occasionally starve the engine of fuel. Steep angles of heel sometimes transfer fuel from the windward to the leeward tank where the engine can't draw on it. The remedies for these troubles are to keep the fuel clean and by all means service the fuel filters. Properly designed valve placement will prevent undesired transfer of fuel from the windward tank.

Seldom does the auto fuel tank get a dose of water. But aqua in the fuel is quite common aboard the auxiliary, and as little as a martini glassful will stop the engine, gasoline or diesel, inboard or outboard.

Your plan for solving the water-in-fuel problem involves two tacks: First, keep water out by using fittings and a layout which block the entrance of water. Second, fit the fuel system with adequate traps and filters to prevent water from reaching the engine's fuel system. We'll have more to say about these matters in subsequent chapters.

Hundreds of gallons of gasoline flow through the tank and fuel system of the family car each year, doing so with relative continuity. However, the tank and system of most auxiliaries handle but a few gills of fuel per season. Worse, the fuel often flows only four months of the year. For the balance of the time liquid simply sits and deteriorates. Two things happen inside the hibernating tank: (1) The fuel sometimes forms tar. When drawn through the system, the tar blocks passages, causes components to stick, and generally gunks up the works. (2) Water forms by condensation of moisture from the air which the tank breathes. The less fuel in the tank, the more it breathes because of temperature and barometric changes. Water itself can stop the engine dead. This we all know. It can also form nasty compounds in conjunction with other products in the fuel, and the ensuing gunk will corrode system components.

Your best bet in minimizing the effects of meager fuel flow is to use fuel tanks of minimum size commensurate with your kind of sailing. Also, empty the tank or tanks at the end of the season so that the fuel does not deteriorate during lay-up. Then, at fitting-out time, purge the system with solvent, getting out all gum, water, and remnants of old fuel. (See Chapter X and XVII for details.)

Sailboat exhaust systems comprise anything from a straight pipe to a complex of tubes, hoses, pipes, and traps. Some systems do their job, directing exhaust overboard while keeping seawater out of the engine. Others, alas, restrict the exhaust or allow dribbles of seawater and condensate to return to the engine, rusting it internally. That's a problem the land vehicle never encounters.

The only avenue of attack you have against engine malaise due to a sour exhaust system is to have the system reworked. This sounds horrendous. Often, however, it's not too much of a job. (See Chapter XIV for details.)

Yes, the sailboat auxiliary is different from the automobile engine both in design and application. We've looked briefly into some of its application problems while hinting at solutions. In the next chapter, we will peer inside the inboard gasoline auxiliary, seeing what makes it tick, while suggesting ways to keep it doing so.

II

Inside the Inboard Gasoline Auxiliary

This chapter does not purport to make you an expert on gasoline marine engines. But from it I do hope you will absorb basics and nomenclature sufficient to allow you to talk comfortably with an engine mechanic or to understand why you make certain adjustments to a motor.

Inside, the gasoline auxiliary is similar to a small automobile engine. In fact, many auxiliaries are compact car engines which have been modified, the most common alterations being improved cooling and exhaust systems, plus a marine transmission. Like your car's engine, the inboard auxiliary is a 4-stroke cycle machine; it's water cooled, and uses the same fuel.

Engine Parts and What They Do

Although most sailors consider the auxiliary a finicky kind of machine, it's really quite uncomplicated. A dozen major parts and assemblies comprise ninety percent of its works. These parts and their respective functions are described in this chapter.

Cylinders: Jokingly called "jugs" by wise-guy mechanics, the cylinders are simply round bores or wells in the engine's cylinder block. There's a cylinder for each piston to slide up and down in, and a great many auxiliaries have four of them. Since the cylinders are an integral part of the engine, deep inside, and part of the basic structure, a broken or cracked cylinder is an expensive trouble, indeed. Most common cause of a fractured cylinder is freezing of water in the cylinder block.

Pistons: Referred to as "buckets" by engine buffs, the pistons are perfectly round metal machinings which fit closely inside their respective cylinders, but are free to slide up and down, reciprocating

5

back and forth as the engine runs. When a piston is at the top of its travel, it's said to be at *top dead center,* or simply *top center.* When at the lower end of its stroke, it's at *bottom center.* You'll note these terms frequently when the timing of an engine is discussed. You'll hear a mechanic say, for example, "The spark is timed when number one piston is at top center."

Function of the piston is to move working gases in and out of the cylinder and to convert combustion pressure into useful work. Consequently, if a piston is damaged or burned, the engine will be very sick, indeed, and its repairs expensive.

Connecting Rods: Con-rods, one to a piston, connect the reciprocating pistons to the crankshaft. Think of a bike rider's knee as his piston; then his shin is the con-rod. The rod's upper end flies up and down with the piston; its lower end spins around with the crankshaft. There's a rod for each piston and cylinder. A broken connecting rod usually disables not only its associated piston, but frequently flails about and smashes other parts of the engine.

Crankshaft: Just as the pedal and its arm convert the bike rider's leg motion to rotary motion, so does the crankshaft convert the piston and con-rod's up and down activity to rotary motion inside the auxiliary. The crankshaft is the engine's backbone, tying the motion of all pistons together and delivering their power to the flywheel. Obviously, a broken crankshaft finishes the engine; but, praise be, cranks seldom fracture.

Flywheel: Simply a heavy steel wheel, the flywheel smooths out the engine's rotation. Its important secondary function is to carry a large-diameter ring gear, often over a foot across. Purpose of the ring gear is to mesh with the self-starter's small pinion gear. This allows the starter to crank the engine by rotating the flywheel. Should the ring gear strip or lose some teeth, the engine cannot be started (except by hand crank).

Valves: Inboards have valves. Outboards don't. They're called *poppet valves,* and they look like steel mushrooms with long stems. Each cylinder has two valves: an inlet or intake valve, and an exhaust. Of the two, the exhaust valve lives the more rigorous life and is most likely to cash in first. Valve functions are to admit explosive mixture to the cylinder (the inlet valve) and allow burned gases to

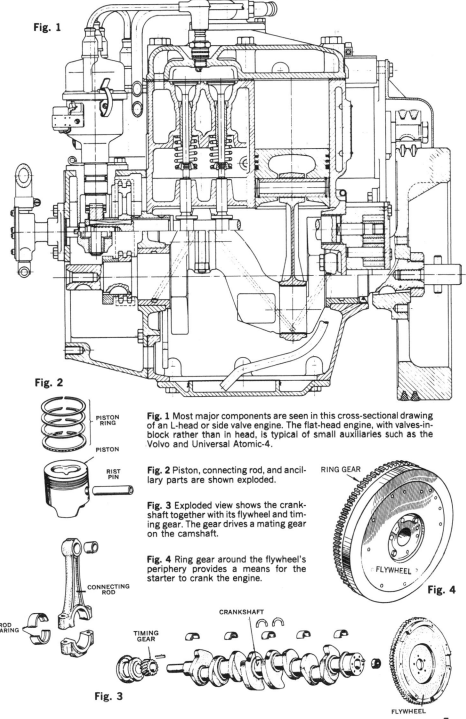

Fig. 1

Fig. 2

PISTON RING

PISTON

RIST PIN

Fig. 1 Most major components are seen in this cross-sectional drawing of an L-head or side valve engine. The flat-head engine, with valves-in-block rather than in head, is typical of small auxiliaries such as the Volvo and Universal Atomic-4.

Fig. 2 Piston, connecting rod, and ancillary parts are shown exploded.

Fig. 3 Exploded view shows the crankshaft together with its flywheel and timing gear. The gear drives a mating gear on the camshaft.

Fig. 4 Ring gear around the flywheel's periphery provides a means for the starter to crank the engine.

RING GEAR

FLYWHEEL

Fig. 4

CONNECTING ROD

ROD BEARING

CRANKSHAFT

TIMING GEAR

FLYWHEEL

Fig. 3

7

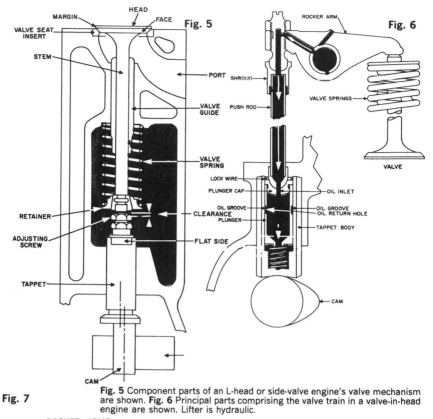

Fig. 5 Component parts of an L-head or side-valve engine's valve mechanism are shown. **Fig. 6** Principal parts comprising the valve train in a valve-in-head engine are shown. Lifter is hydraulic.

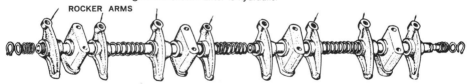

Fig. 7 Rocker arms are shown. These actuate the valves in a valve-in-head engine.

escape (the exhaust valve). Details on valve function follow a few paragraphs hence. Suffice it to say, if a valve sticks open, burns, or leaks, the cylinder which it serves will deliver little useful work.

Camshaft: Driven by the crankshaft via gears or a chain, the camshaft rotates at half engine speed. On this shaft are bumps, called cams, which push the valves open in the proper sequence. There is one cam per valve. Should the adjustable distance between cam and valve lifting mechanism be excessive, the valve will tap. Should that distance (clearance) be too small, the valve may malfunction and be damaged. Then the engine will run rough, maybe quit altogether.

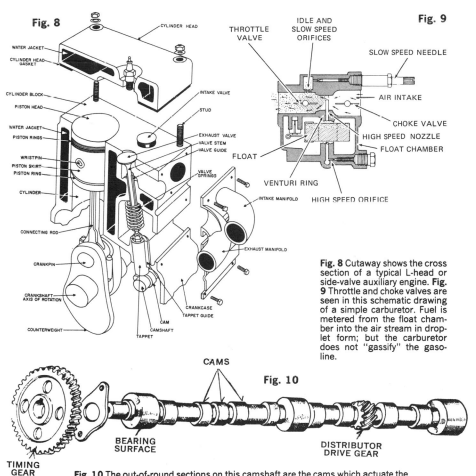

Fig. 8 Cutaway shows the cross section of a typical L-head or side-valve auxiliary engine. **Fig. 9** Throttle and choke valves are seen in this schematic drawing of a simple carburetor. Fuel is metered from the float chamber into the air stream in droplet form; but the carburetor does not "gassify" the gasoline.

Fig. 10 The out-of-round sections on this camshaft are the cams which actuate the valves. Driving the shaft at half engine speed, the gear meshes with a mating gear on the crankshaft.

When a mechanic speaks of "adjusting the valves," he's referring to adjusting the clearance or distance between the cam and valve follower. Its magnitude is on the order of one-hundredth of an inch.

Valve Spring: A cam pushes each valve open. Its spring forces it closed. If the spring weakens, the engine falters at high speed. If the spring breaks, the valve ceases to function; the engine usually quits. It's as simple as that.

Rocker Arm: In a valve-in-head engine, the rocker arm, looking like a walking beam, transmits cam motion to valve lift. Valve clearance adjusting screws are often found in the rocker arm. Should the

9

arm break (it seldom does) the valve is put out of action.

Carburetor: What a misunderstood and abused device: Its purpose is simple, but its function and parts are critical. The carburetor is a mixer, blending air and gasoline to form an explosive mixture. Its entire function is to mix gasoline and air so they can be burned in the cylinders and create power. The carb doesn't "gasify" or atomize; it just mixes, and as long as it does its job, the engine has a fighting chance. If the carb passes too much air and not enough gasoline, the engine loses power, pops back, barks, coughs, overheats its exhaust valves, dies. Should the device pass too much gasoline and insufficient air, the engine belches black smoke, gags, loses power, runs rough, dies.

Choke: The choke is a butterfly valve, a round disc, which when closed, reduces the volume of air admitted to the carburetor's mixing section. When air is reduced, proportionately more gasoline flows to the engine, and the mixture is termed "rich."

Operated by a temperature sensor, spring, and linkage, the automatic choke enriches the mixture when the engine is cold, and does so automatically. Operated by hand via a cable, the manual choke enriches the mixture whenever you want. That should be only when the engine is cold. We all know the effects of too much choking: flooding, stalling, hard starting, and swearing by the operator.

Fuel Pump: Functioning like one of those diaphragm-type bilge pumps, the fuel pump draws gasoline from the fuel tank, delivering it to the carburetor. Operating pressure is typically four pounds per square inch. Granted, that's not a great deal of pressure, but should the pressure fall substantially, or should the pump fail, the carburetor starves, and the engine stops dead as a stone.

Distributor: Possibly the most violently attacked device in all the sailing world is the distributor on the sailboat's auxiliary. Certainly it is cranky because it handles high-voltage electricity; and Lord knows HV electricity and the marine environment hate each other.

The distributor performs two functions, separate but related: Via its points—a low-voltage switch—it determines the time at which sparks jump the spark plug gaps inside the cylinders. Spark occurs at the exact instant which the points open, break, part company. Spark does not originate when the points close. The points' switch

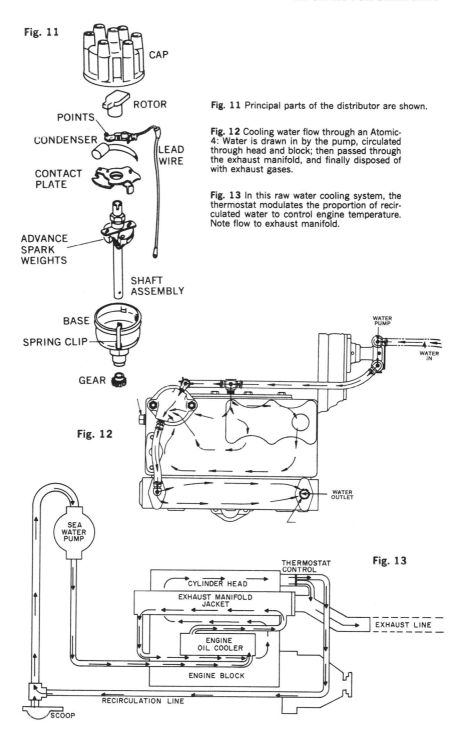

Fig. 11

CAP

ROTOR

POINTS

CONDENSER

LEAD WIRE

CONTACT PLATE

ADVANCE SPARK WEIGHTS

SHAFT ASSEMBLY

BASE

SPRING CLIP

GEAR

Fig. 11 Principal parts of the distributor are shown.

Fig. 12 Cooling water flow through an Atomic-4: Water is drawn in by the pump, circulated through head and block; then passed through the exhaust manifold, and finally disposed of with exhaust gases.

Fig. 13 In this raw water cooling system, the thermostat modulates the proportion of recirculated water to control engine temperature. Note flow to exhaust manifold.

Fig. 12

WATER PUMP

WATER IN

WATER OUTLET

SEA WATER PUMP

THERMOSTAT CONTROL

Fig. 13

CYLINDER HEAD

EXHAUST MANIFOLD JACKET

EXHAUST LINE

ENGINE OIL COOLER

ENGINE BLOCK

RECIRCULATION LINE

SCOOP

11

function is thus backward from what one might expect.

Through its rotor and cap, the device distributes spark to the correct cylinders in sequence. The top area of the distributor is a rotary high-voltage selector switch.

A description of distributor troubles would fill page after page. We'll cover the ills in later chapters. Suffice it to say that sickness in the points causes missing, popping, knocking, stalling, poor idling, bad timing and generally poor performance. Malfunctions of the distributor cap and rotor cause hard starting, stalling, missing, and death in damp weather.

Cooling System: The auxiliary engine's cooling system resembles that of a car engine in some respects, but is quite different in others. In both kinds of engine, cooling water is circulated through the block and head, taking away waste heat. In the car, heat is dissipated to the surrounding air by the radiator. The boat engine, however, transfers its surplus heat to the water in which the yacht floats.

The cooling system comprises a series of passages, pipes, and tubes through which water is pumped. In the simplest engines, water is sucked out of the sea, circulated through the engine, squirted into the exhaust pipe, and dumped overboard. Principal moving part is the water pump (some engines have two) and the other moving part is a thermostat, which regulates engine temperatures by throttling the flow of water.

Cooling system failure stops the auxiliary motor even faster than it does the automobile engine. This is so because the auxiliary works harder, is buried in a hole with little ventilation, and depends upon water to cool its exhaust. As most yachtsmen know, the principal cause of cooling failure is a clogged water inlet, often following a grounding. Other causes of overheating are a broken or loose V-belt, defective thermostat, malfunctioning water pump, or ruptured water hose.

Exhaust Manifold: Attached tightly to the side of the engine, the exhaust manifold is a set of cast pipes collecting the hot exhaust gases which spew from the engine's cylinders. At its downstream terminus, it delivers the spent matter to the exhaust pipe. The exhaust manifold in your boat's auxiliary is much different from the one in your car. Under the Detroit hood, the manifold is simply a bare casting, exposed to the air. But on the marine power plant, the manifolds are water-cooled, comprising a set of complete castings incorporating liquid-carrying jackets. A copious volume of water is pumped through the exhaust manifold jackets, carrying away tremendous heat.

"How come?" asked one knowledgeable yachtsman. "Why is the exhaust manifold a simple open casting on my car, but water-cooled on my auxiliary?"

Perched at the front end of a car behind the cooling fan, the auto's exhaust manifold is adequately cooled by the rushing stream of air. (Even so, it runs terribly hot.) Not so lucky is the auxiliary's exhaust. It swelters in the bilge area with little ventilation. What's more, for its size, it handles far more hot exhaust than the car's pipes. Marine engines work harder: Propelling a boat takes a lot of push, and there are no hills to coast down. Were the marine manifold not cooled, it would run red hot and constitute a fire hazard. That's why it's water jacketed.

The most common trouble encountered with an exhaust manifold is that it breaks, cracks, or springs a leak. The two most common causes of manifold rupture are freezing of trapped water, and abuse due to overheating. Manifolds can sometimes be repaired, but alas, in most instances they are replaced. Because they are complex castings, because they are "marine," and because the assembly generally includes both inlet and exhaust manifolds in one, they are expensive.

Inlet Manifold: It's sometimes called an "intake manifold," and its function is to conduct the gasoline-air mixture from carburetor to cylinders. Often cast integral with the exhaust manifold, it is warmed by exhaust heat to help vaporize droplets of gasoline passing through. Sometimes an otherwise innocent-looking intake manifold will spring a leak, or its mounting gaskets leak. Then the engine will idle fast but rough, starting will get difficult, and the engine may miss at part throttle.

Exhaust Pipe: Strictly speaking, the exhaust pipe is not an integral engine component, but it's so much a part of the picture, that it should be included in the parts description.

The sailboat auxiliary exhaust pipe not only conducts hot gas away from the engine, it also carries spent cooling water overboard.

After passing through the engine and exhaust manifold, heated water is spewed into the exhaust pipe. The flow of exhaust gas then carries the coolant out the stack. The arrangement is appropriate because the flow of water cools the pipe which would run dangerously hot if not cooled; and the pipe, returning the favor, provides a convenient means for ejecting the water. Because it does double duty, the pipe's design and maintenance must be of high order. A sick exhaust can ruin the engine, sink the boat or asphyxiate the crew. More about exhaust maintenance and possible modification follows in subsequent chapters.

Lubrication System: The lowest part of the engine is called the crankcase, and the bottom of the crankcase is the oil pan. It's in the oil pan that lubricating oil is stored, and from the oil pan a gear pump sucks up lube, forcing it through the engine's moving parts. The oil then dribbles back to the pan which technical people sometimes call a *sump*. Lubrication accessories include an oil cooler and a filter, both of which we'll discuss later.

Since marine engine parts are highly loaded and sometimes spin quite fast, a decent lubrication system is essential. On the sailboat auxiliary, the basic system seldom fails. However, if the oil level is allowed to get low, the lube system may not do its job if the engine is run when the boat is heeling. Also, if the engine is run too briefly, never being allowed to attain full warmth, the oiling system may get gunked up with sludge and may quit doing its essential job.

Transmission: Sometimes called the "clutch" or "reverse gear," the marine transmission is different from the one in your car. It has one forward and one reverse speed. Sometimes it incorporates reduction gears allowing the engine to swing a bigger, more efficient propeller. Sometimes it has an oil cooler. Generally, the transmission is reliable, and if you avoid slamming it into reverse when going full bore ahead, it'll often outlast the engine.

How the Engine Parts Function Together

You've an idea, perhaps a mite fuzzy, of the cylinders, pistons, valves, carburetor, distributor, manifolds and other components that make your auxiliary tick. Read on, then, while we review how these parts cooperate to make your auxiliary run.

Whether your engine has one, two, four, or more cylinders, each

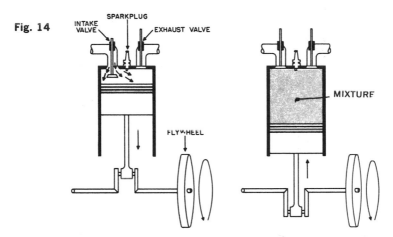

Fig. 14

Fig. 14 Intake stroke: Combustible mixture is drawn through the open intake valve by the descending piston. When the piston reverses travel at bottom center, the valves are closed.

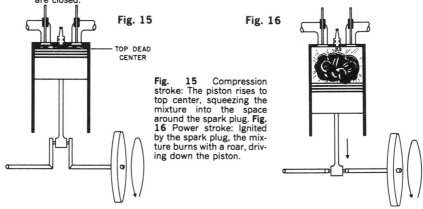

Fig. 15   Fig. 16

Fig. 15 Compression stroke: The piston rises to top center, squeezing the mixture into the space around the spark plug. **Fig. 16** Power stroke: Ignited by the spark plug, the mixture burns with a roar, driving down the piston.

Fig. 17 Exhaust stroke: Near bottom center, the exhaust valve opens; then the piston rises, driving out the spent gases.

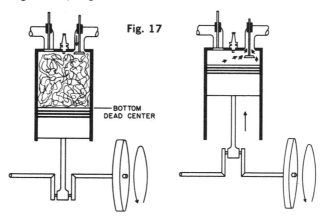

Fig. 17

repeats the same series of operations over and over again. The more cylinders, the smoother the engine runs; but the theory remains the same. When you learn to visualize what's going on in one cylinder, you know them all. It's just that they work in sequence. The start of each sequence or "cycle" is the intake stroke. In a nutshell, here's how the cycle looks. (Understanding the basic cycle helps you keep the monster running, helps you fix it when you've got to. It's like understanding how the trim and set of a sail affect its driving power.)

Intake: The inlet valve opens, setting the stage for the function. The piston then descends on intake stroke, sucking combustible mixture into the cylinder. To reach the space, the gasoline-air mixture has flowed from the carburetor, through the intake manifold and open inlet valve. As the descending piston approaches the bottom of its travel, bottom dead center, the intake valve closes, sealing the cylinder volume and preventing escape of mixture during the next upward piston stroke. Among the engine troubles which originate during intake are rough running or stalling because the mixture is too lean. A lean mixture does not have sufficient gasoline content to burn well. Another trouble is engine flooding because the mix is too rich. Yet another is insufficient flow of mixture to fill the cylinder to required pressure. This could be caused by gross lack of ventilation in the engine compartment or perhaps because the intake valve is incorrectly timed.

Compression: Both valves are closed as the piston rises in its cylinder, compressing the mixture ahead of its dome, squeezing the mixture tightly into the valve compartment or combustion chamber. During compression stroke, the working matter—the mixture—swirls turbulently while being heated by compression. During this stroke, remaining miniscule droplets of gasoline are evaporated, and by completion of compression stroke, the working matter is ready for ignition.

Several engine troubles have their origin during the compression stroke. If the piston does not seal snug in its cylinder, if the piston rings or cylinder are worn, gas will leak past the piston during compression. Leaking causes "loss of compression," reducing the engine's power. Leaks also force gasoline down into the crankcase where it dilutes the oil. Much worse, gasoline which has sneaked down to the crankcase can explode. But don't be alarmed, this only happens when the piston is terribly worn.

If either the intake or exhaust valve leaks, compression pressure suffers, mixture is lost, and engine power sags. If, during compression, mixture is ignited by an unwanted hot spot, such as an overheated exhaust valve, *bang!* goes preignition. The mixture explodes prematurely, making the engine knock, while severely stressing its parts.

Power: This stroke is the payoff. At the end of compression, when the piston reaches top center, the spark plug sends out a little zap of electric spark. Instantly, the combustible mixture is ignited, and burns like a tornado. Pressure of the roaring flame pushes hard on the piston, forcing it down on power stroke. Naturally, during this dynamic period, both valves are closed.

Every imaginable performance trouble is given birth in the power stroke. If the exhaust valve leaks, hot gases force their way through and erode it to death. The engine stops. If the spark fails, if it is anemic, or snaps out at the wrong time, the power stroke is either weak or non-existent. If the spark is too early, the gasoline low in octane, or the engine overheated, the mixture may explode violently or detonate. Power is lost and the engine may be damaged by the resulting knock. If the spark is late, the mixture will continue burning hotly to the end of the working stroke, and will burn the exhaust valve. Maybe it will also make the engine bark back through the carburetor. But possibly, just possibly, despite Murphy's Law, all will go well throughout the power stroke and the engine will run like a dream.

Exhaust: As the piston approaches bottom center on its power stroke, the exhaust valve opens; hot, inert products of combustion, still under pressure, surge out the valve's opening. The valve then remains open as the piston rises, pushing hot material out of the cylinder. When the piston reaches top center, the exhaust valve closes. At this point, the inlet valve commences to open, and the cylinder is ready to repeat its entire cycle of intake, compression, power, and exhaust.

Engine troubles directly traceable to the exhaust stroke are few, since the stroke stages an innocuous performance. However, blue smoke from the exhaust is caused by burning oil, the smoke of which dilutes exhaust products. Exhaust valves are burned during this stroke, also. However, the trouble originates during other strokes, such as late ignition timing in the power stroke.

In this chapter we examined the major components which constitute the gasoline auxiliary engine. We also saw how the pistons, cylinders, and valves work together in the four-stroke cycle, generating power and sometimes creating trouble. In the following chapter, we'll look into the inboard diesel, see what makes it tick, and consider its problems in light of Murphy's Law.

III

Inside the Diesel Auxiliary

If you haven't already done so, please peruse Chapter II which deals with the gasoline inboard auxiliary before reading this chapter. Even though you may not be particularly interested in the gasoline engine, in the present chapter we will use a number of terms which were defined in the previous one. We'll also draw analogies between the two kinds of power.

The diesel is a tough customer.

While the gasoline auxiliary resembles the auto engine, and indeed is sometimes a modification of it, the diesel auxiliary is like an industrial machine. Heavy, reliable, tenacious: that's the diesel.

Compared to the gasoline marine engine, the diesel is safer, more economical, more reliable, but smellier. It requires less fixing than its gasoline counterpart. However, when serious repairs are needed, they require more precision and are harder and more expensive to obtain.

The diesel is safe because it burns hard-to-ignite furnace oil, not gasoline. Discussing this aspect, one of our friends summed up his feelings by saying: "If I throw a lighted match into an open pail of diesel fuel, the match is extinguished by the liquid. If I throw it into an open pail of gasoline, I'm lucky to escape with my life from the raging inferno that follows."

The diesel is reliable because it harbors no electric ignition, no distributor, no spark plugs, and no high voltage. It is devoid of a carburetor. Certainly ignition and carburetion are the most troublesome systems on the conventional gasoline engine. Eliminating them makes the diesel more seaworthy.

On the diesel, a high-pressure fuel injection system, completely sealed, replaces both carburetion and electric ignition. Provided that its connections are kept tight, that it is not physically mauled (as by having a tool bashed into it) and that it is fed clean fuel, the injection system is extremely reliable. We'll crawl out on a limb and state that diesel is twice as reliable as gasoline. The reason is that the hermetically-sealed injection is less vulnerable to seawater attack than the electric ignition and carburetor found on the gasoline machine.

Heavier, tougher components make the diesel more immune to trouble. Most diesel auxiliaries were born as small industrial or pickup truck engines, and their heritage shows in ruggedness. The little oil burner's exhaust is several hundred degrees cooler than that of a gasoline engine, sometimes making things cooler under the deck. And that's a small advantage, too, particularly for the sailor sleeping aft in a quarter bunk near the exhaust pipe.

Although two-stroke-cycle diesels are built, the Detroit (GM) engine being a famous example, most small auxiliary motors are four-stroke machines. It is this kind of engine which we treat in this chapter.

Engine Parts and What They Do

In roughly the same order as we discussed gasoline engine parts and components, we review diesel equivalents, with a discussion of injection components replacing our remarks on the distributor, carburetor and related items.

Cylinders: In some diesels, the cylinders are cast integral with the rest of the engine block, as in a gasoline motor. In others, however, reflecting their industrial background, cylinders are iron or steel liners, made very tough and designed to be replaceable when worn. From a maintenance standpoint, it is desirable to have an engine with replaceable cylinder liners. Good as they are, however, cylinder liners are subject to the workings of Murphy's Law: Sometimes they don't seal properly in the engine block. Then water leaks from the cooling jacket down into the oil pan; and that's the end of cruising under power until the engine is torn apart and repaired.

Pistons: Diesel pistons are practically indistinguishable from the ones in a gasoline engine. A little heavier, perhaps, and sometimes having a special shape to the crown (top), the diesel piston is still a cat of the same stripe as that in the gasoline engine. And it performs

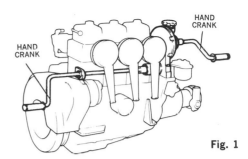

Fig. 1 Hand cranking from either end is possible on this Volvo 3-cylinder diesel. Compression is released as manual cranking accelerates heavy flywheel.

Fig. 1

essentially the same function.

Connecting Rods: The diesel's con-rods are the same as those in a gasoline auxiliary, just stronger and beefier.

Crankshaft: Like the pistons and rods, the diesel crankshaft closely resembles that in a gasoline engine, except it has bigger sections and is proportionately heavier.

Flywheel: Carrying the starter ring gear, the diesel flywheel is heavier than that on a gas engine because the diesel's compression ratio is higher. Compression ratio expresses how tightly the working matter is squeezed or compressed into the combustion space at the end of the compression stroke. In the diesel the squeeze is tighter. Therefore the flywheel is heavier, having sufficient momentum to carry the piston up on its compression stroke. Should the flywheel be too light, the machine would run rough at low speeds.

Valves and Springs: Both intake and exhaust valves work a little easier in the diesel than in the gasoline job. The exhaust valve, in particular, runs cooler and gives less trouble.

Camshaft and Rocker Arms: Diesels run slower than gasoline engines, as a rule; consequently the valve mechanisms are stressed commensurately less. Troubles are fewer in the valve train.

Injection System: Eliminating both carburetor and distributor, diesel injection performs the function of both: It meters a correct volume of fuel to the cylinders, and it times the instant of ignition. High-pressure injector nozzles replace spark plugs, while extreme pressure tubing substitutes for high-voltage ignition wiring.

Heart of the diesel's injection system are the injection pumps, one pump for each cylinder. In some machines, the pumps are grouped

21

together in an assembly on the side of the engine. From this assembly one high-pressure tube runs to each cylinder. On other engines, there is a small pump mounted on top of each cylinder, actuated by the camshaft.

One in each cylinder, injector nozzles replace the gasoline engine's spark plugs. They are high-pressure pinhole jets which squirt a little fuel into each cylinder, atomizing it at exactly the right moment.

High-pressure pumps, injectors, and associated fuel-carrying tubing comprise the principal parts of the diesel's fuel and ignition system. In a moment we will explain how they function in the cycle. As for potential troubles, the two greatest are caused by dirt in the fuel and leaks in the system, in that order. A little dirt will stop the engine, and a bad leak may do so, as well.

Fuel Pump: In addition to the high-pressure injector pumps, a low-pressure transfer pump is found on most diesels. Its function is to draw fuel oil from the tank, delivering it to the injector pumps. In some engines, surplus fuel not consumed by the injection pumps is returned via a drain-off tube to the fuel tank. The returned fuel is warm. That's why you will sometimes feel a warm fuel tank on a diesel yacht after she has been running for several hours. Both diaphragm and gear pumps are used as fuel-transfer units. In either case, if the pump fails, the engine starves and quits, as a gasoline auxiliary stops when its fuel pump gives up the ghost.

Cooling System: "Fresh-water" or closed-circuit cooling is used on a substantial majority of diesels, in keeping with their long-life industrial image. A pair of water pumps circulates two separate and distinct coolants. One pump, often a centrifugal model such as is found on car and truck engines, circulates fresh water through the engine and its accessories. This clean, unsalted water is usually mixed with glycol and rust inhibitor. A second pump, commonly of the vane or gear variety, sucks up seawater and circulates it through a heat exchanger. The heat exchange unit serves exactly the same purpose as the radiator in a car, cooling the hot engine water. However, rather than transferring engine heat to air, the heat exchanger transfers it to seawater pumped through its core. Naturally, the engine's fresh water and seawater are never allowed to intermix.

The beauty of closed-circuit engine cooling is that only potable

Fig. 2

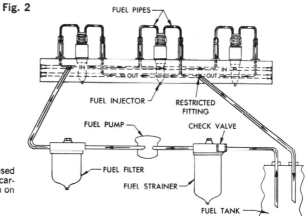

Fig. 2 A hermetically closed fuel system replaced both carburetor and ignition system on the diesel.

Fig. 3

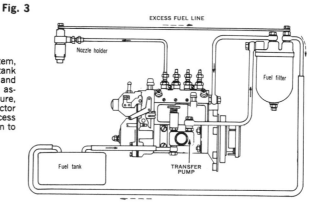

Fig. 3 In this typical system, diesel fuel flows from the tank through the transfer pump and filter to the injector pump assembly. At very high pressure, fuel is forced to the injector nozzle into the cylinder. Excess flows back to the filter, then to the tank.

Fig. 4

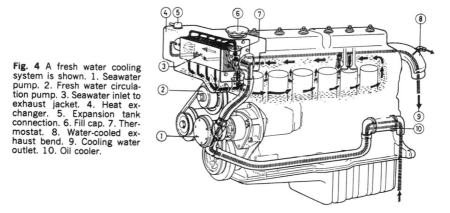

Fig. 4 A fresh water cooling system is shown. 1. Seawater pump. 2. Fresh water circulation pump. 3. Seawater inlet to exhaust jacket. 4. Heat exchanger. 5. Expansion tank connection. 6. Fill cap. 7. Thermostat. 8. Water-cooled exhaust bend. 9. Cooling water outlet. 10. Oil cooler.

23

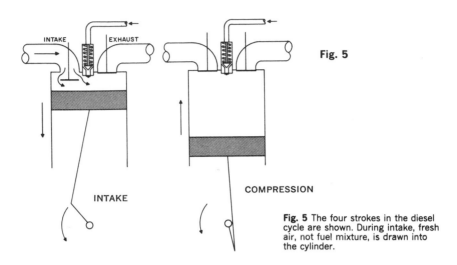

Fig. 5

Fig. 5 The four strokes in the diesel cycle are shown. During intake, fresh air, not fuel mixture, is drawn into the cylinder.

water is allowed to touch the engine's innards. Such coolant doesn't rust or corrode expensive engine parts. The machinery enjoys longer life and is more reliable. In addition, coolant temperature is more uniform throughout the system, making for more efficient engine operation.

Exhaust Manifold: The diesel's exhaust manifold is just about indistinguishable from that on a gasoline auxiliary. It performs the same function. Internally, it runs a little cooler because diesel exhaust gases are milder than those from a gasoline engine. But from a practical standpoint, the difference is negligible. The same applies to the exhaust pipe.

Inlet Manifold: There's quite a difference between the gasoline engine inlet manifold and that on the diesel. While the manifold on the gas burner handles fuel-air mixture and is heated, the diesel's manifold handles nothing but pure air and is not heated. Rather than terminating at a carburetor, it ends at a simple air cleaner, the function of which is to keep flies, mosquitoes, and lint out of the engine's cylinders. Beautiful simplicity.

Lubrication System: Differences between lubrication systems on diesel and gasoline engines are simply in small details. Essentially they are the same.

Transmission: The clutch, reverse, and reduction gears are some-

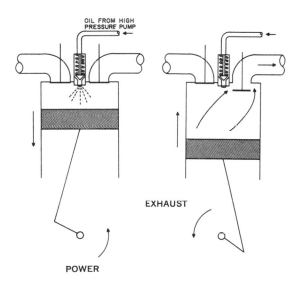

what tougher in the diesel transmission because, for a given horse-power, the diesel offers higher torque than the gasoline engine. Beefier components are required to handle the added "twist," but basic functions are the same as for the gas burner, and so, alas, are the troubles.

How Diesel Parts Function Together

The four-stroke diesel resembles its gasoline cousin, but there are basic differences. These will be apparent as we examine the diesel's sequence of piston strokes.

Intake: The piston is at top dead center and the intake valve is starting to open. Down goes the diesel's piston on intake stroke, and through its valve whistles an unrestricted gush of plain, fresh air. When the piston completes intake stroke, the cylinder is filled with air. There's no fuel intermixed; the air is not throttled, heated, or carbureted. It's as nature made it. Indeed, if diesel trouble originates in the intake stroke, it's usually because the air is dirty, restricted, or contaminated. If the air supply is choked off, the diesel loses power and smokes.

At the end of this stroke, the inlet valve closes, sealing the air in the cylinder, and preparing for the following upward stroke.

Compression: Both valves are tightly closed during compression stroke as the piston ascends. Up goes the piston, squashing the trapped air into a small space at the top of the cylinder. This space is tiny, making compression pressure terrific. Such extreme compression of the air heats it far hotter than the mixture in a gasoline engine when it's compressed. Heat of compression in a diesel is vital to its operation.

We have all heard discussions of compression ratio. For example, someone will say, "That engine has a high compression ratio." The term describes the ratio of entire cylinder volume to volume of compressed working matter at the completion of compression stroke. Typical ratio in a gasoline engine is 8:1. But diesel ratios are much higher, 16:1 or even 20:1 being typical. In short, one of the principal differences between gasoline and diesel is the diesel's higher compression. Both pressure and temperature are extreme when air is compressed in the diesel.

That suggests the troubles which spring from faulty compression. If valve or piston rings are defective, allowing compression pressure to leak off, compression temperature is reduced; then the engine will either behave badly or will fail to run at all. Good compression is essential to the diesel.

Power: The stage is set for the power stroke at the completion of compression.

Both valves are closed; the combustion chamber above the piston is filled with swirling, hot gas. Now, just as the piston's crown approaches top center, the fuel injector spits an atomized stream of fuel oil into the waiting hot air. So high is the air temperature that the mist of fuel bursts into a roaring flame, still further increasing temperature and pressure, and thrusting the piston down on its useful power stroke.

In the diesel, timing and duration of fuel injection are important, just as important as spark timing in a gasoline motor. Fuel must begin squirting into the combustion space just a few degrees before the piston reaches top center. It must continue for only so many degrees after the piston starts down on its payoff stroke. Smoke, knock, and loss of power plague the engine having a poorly adjusted injection system. If injection is early, the engine will lose power, may even be damaged. If it is late, the engine may knock, lose power and refuse to start and run.

Exhaust: While the piston is still on power stroke, but approaching bottom center, the exhaust valve opens. Out rush the products of combustion into the exhaust manifold and out the tail pipe. The piston then rises, pushing out remaining gases and scavenging the cylinder during its upward travel. Reaching top center, the piston completes its exhaust function and is ready to descend on the next intake stroke, repeating the cycle.

Gasoline and Diesel Compared

The diesel auxiliary is heavier and tougher than the gasoline engine, and because it burns furnace oil, you can usually smell its presence. Because it has no distributor or carburetor, it is more reliable. It is safer than the gasoline burner because its fuel is more difficult to ignite. It turns slower, has higher compression, cooler exhaust, and is more economical, using less fuel for a given horsepower. Because of the safety aspect, there are skippers who will venture afloat with no other kind of auxiliary power.

IV

Inside the
Outboard Auxiliary

Although it is something of an aesthetic blight on the transom of a pretty sailboat, the outboard motor provides auxiliary propulsion for thousands of small yachts. Armadas of sailing craft below 25 feet are seen to have kickers rather than inboards. Why?

Compared to the inboard auxiliary, the outboard is cheaper, simpler to install, and takes less space. On an equal-power basis it is lighter than an inboard; and when the boat is underway, its propeller can be retracted, causing no drag. New outboards are very quiet. And one of the undeniably great things about outboard power is that when the machine gets really sick and needs professional attention, it can be removed from the boat and taken to a shop. It's always much cheaper and easier to take an ailing motor to the mechanic than to have that friendly fellow make a house call.

Those are some of the advantages. On the negative side, unless boxed, the motor is horribly exposed to the elements, its weight on the transom throws the small boat off balance, it is hard to reach for tinkering, and if it has an integral fuel tank, it is hard to gas-up without dribbling gasoline.

As to reliability in the pinches, that depends to a large extent on where and how the motor is mounted. If in a well, resembling a big square centerboard well, the motor is probably as reliable as an inboard gasoline auxiliary, except in some instances, where it can be starved for air. But if mounted on a bracket hung on the transom, the motor is highly vulnerable to the effects of spray and rain, and its reliability is certainly lessened.

On a horsepower-hour basis, the outboard uses more fuel than either the inboard gasoline engine or diesel. This is usually of rela-

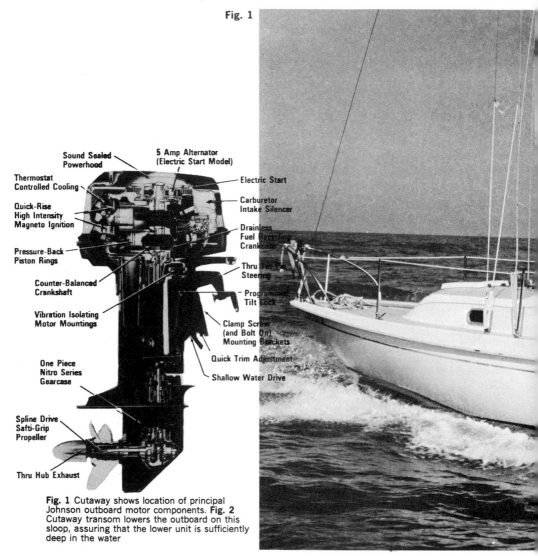

Fig. 1

Sound Sealed Powerhood

5 Amp Alternator (Electric Start Model)

Thermostat Controlled Cooling

Electric Start

Quick-Rise High Intensity Magneto Ignition

Carburetor Intake Silencer

Drainless Fuel Recycling Crankcase

Pressure-Back Piston Rings

Thru Tilt Pin Steering

Counter-Balanced Crankshaft

Programmed Tilt Lock

Vibration Isolating Motor Mountings

Clamp Screw (and Bolt On) Mounting Brackets

One Piece Nitro Series Gearcase

Quick Trim Adjustment

Shallow Water Drive

Spline Drive Safti-Grip Propeller

Thru Hub Exhaust

Fig. 1 Cutaway shows location of principal Johnson outboard motor components. **Fig. 2** Cutaway transom lowers the outboard on this sloop, assuring that the lower unit is sufficiently deep in the water

tively little importance, since the total hours per season on most sailboat engines is inconsequential. However, if the boat is frequently used under power, limited cruising range and increased fuel costs are something to consider.

As we saw in previous chapters, the inboard auxiliary is a four-stroke-cycle engine, usually based upon an automobile or small industrial engine. In many instances, it is a modification of some other kind of power.

Not so the outboard: It is pure marine from start to finish; it's not a modified anything, and it does not use the same kind of engine as land machinery. Its powerhead is a two-stroke cycle motor, simpler and having fewer moving parts than the conventional engine.

Outboard Parts and What They Do

Before determining what makes the outboard tick, and what sometimes keeps it from tocking, a brief description of its parts is in order:

Cylinders: Cylinders in an outboard motor's power head are much different from those in the conventional inboard four-stroke cycle engine. In the outboard, no valves are seen in the combustion space at the top, but holes or ports are found in both sides near the bottom. The machine does not breathe through valves, but through cylinder ports, as we shall see. Some outboard-motor troubles start right with the basic cylinder when its ports become partially clogged. When that happens, the engine can't breathe properly; it loses power and may even die.

Pistons: The outboard piston incorporates a baffle or deflector cast integral with its top or crown. Purpose of the baffle is to work in conjunction with the cylinder ports, directing inlet and exhaust gases so they will flow most efficiently. Outboard pistons are subject to pretty much the same ills as those in an inboard. However, if the operator forgets to mix oil in his gasoline, the pistons will overheat, scuff, wear, and seize. This spells doomsday for the whole machine.

Connecting Rods: Aside from being smaller than those in the inboard, con-rods are quite standard.

Crankshaft: Operating vertically rather than horizontally, the outboard crankshaft converts reciprocating piston activity into useful rotary motion in the usual manner. However, it is mounted in its crankcase such that each section, called a "throw," is sealed off from every other one. It's almost as though every cylinder, piston, and section of crankshaft were a small separate engine. Such special construction has to do with the motor's breathing *modus operandi* which we will presently examine.

Flywheel: Fitted to the upper end of the crankshaft at the top of the outboard, the flywheel carries a ring gear for the starter motor pinion gear. On non-electric, hand-starting rigs, the ring gear is missing, but there's a groove for the starter rope. Alternately, an automatic rope rewind mechanism is seen. We like the rewind starter cord, helping you make more starting yanks per minute when the engine is balky—which it's likely to be on a damp morning when its ignition is wet.

Valves, Camshaft and Rocker Arms: There aren't any.

Carburetor: Not much different from the one on your car's engine, though smaller, the carb performs the same function, metering gaso-

Fig. 3 Dual ignition coils and electric starter are seen on this Chrysler outboard auxiliary.

line and air for combustion. But while the carburetors on auto and inboard engines have limited adjustment devices, outboard carbs sometimes have more. These can be helpful to the sailor having some remote idea what he's doing, and can be a pain in the neck to others who are more interested in boom vangs and halyards than in mechanical propulsion.

Choke: An enriching valve, same as on the inboard, the choke can be manually or electrically operated. Either, if correctly used, will help start a cold engine. If abused, it will flood the machine.

Fuel Pump: The simplest outboards, those with an integral, top-mounted tank, have no fuel pump. Gravity delivers the gasoline to the carb, and there is a screw-type air valve in the filler cap and a butterfly valve on the fuel line. But outboards with remote tanks have a fuel pump to draw gasoline from the tank and deliver it through a hose to the carburetor. When the pump is sick or the tubes don't function properly, the engine won't start. If it's running when the malfunction occurs, it quits.

Distributor: Larger outboards have a distributor something like that on an inboard engine. Some have a magneto, a sort of high voltage generator, usually comprising part of the flywheel. And some have electronic ignition, using transistors and black boxes. All types work just fine until soaked; then they get consumption. On outboards manufactured in the past few years, however, ignition is surprisingly reliable in the face of the worst conditions. When modern systems get soaked, they respond more promptly to drying-out than those of yesteryear, a special blessing for the sailor.

Cooling System: Outboards are cooled by circulating water systems not too unlike those in the inboard. Seawater is drawn by a pump in the lower unit, circulated through the engine, then dumped overboard. Probably the most common cause of trouble is clogging of the water intake. A second cause is failure of the water pump.

Exhaust System: "Relatively quiet," describes the exhaust from the modern outboard auxiliary. Exhaust gases leaving the cylinder are shot down to the lower unit, mixed with water, and buried below the surface. Some lower units direct the exhaust through the center of the propeller hub, others squirt it out of a duct above or behind the prop. All rigs do the job efficiently, and little ever goes wrong.

Lower Unit: Outboards and outdrives have lower units; inboards don't. Comprising the vertical drive shaft, reduction gears, horizontal drive shaft and propeller, the unit is sheathed in a light metal casting. Most outboards have a reverse gear and clutch, these components being in the lower unit. Most lower unit troubles originate with insufficient lubrication in the gearcase. Others are caused by the prop walloping an underwater obstruction or the shift mechanism throwing in the towel because of mysterous manifestations.

How Engine Parts Function Together

Describing functions in the conventional four-stroke cycle engine, we traced *intake, compression, power, exhaust* in that order, for both gasoline and diesel. We can't do this for the outboard's two-stroke cycle because for each power stroke there is but one upward sweep of the piston. Each single stroke in the outboard must perform the function of two in the four-stroke engine.

Power-Exhaust: Consider what happens just at the instant the spark plug snaps out its bit of fire: The combustion space is filled with

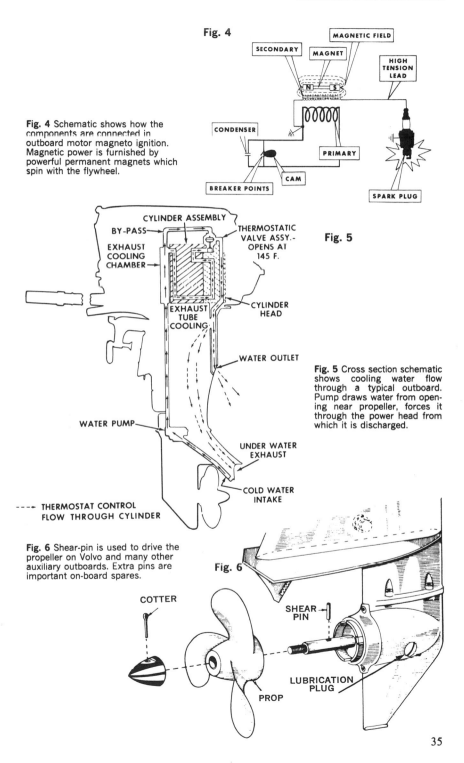

Fig. 4

MAGNETIC FIELD

SECONDARY   MAGNET

HIGH TENSION LEAD

N   S

CONDENSER

PRIMARY

BREAKER POINTS   CAM

SPARK PLUG

Fig. 4 Schematic shows how the components are connected in outboard motor magneto ignition. Magnetic power is furnished by powerful permanent magnets which spin with the flywheel.

CYLINDER ASSEMBLY

BY-PASS

THERMOSTATIC VALVE ASSY.- OPENS AT 145 F.

Fig. 5

EXHAUST COOLING CHAMBER

EXHAUST TUBE COOLING

CYLINDER HEAD

WATER OUTLET

Fig. 5 Cross section schematic shows cooling water flow through a typical outboard. Pump draws water from opening near propeller, forces it through the power head from which it is discharged.

WATER PUMP

UNDER WATER EXHAUST

COLD WATER INTAKE

- - - THERMOSTAT CONTROL FLOW THROUGH CYLINDER

Fig. 6 Shear-pin is used to drive the propeller on Volvo and many other auxiliary outboards. Extra pins are important on-board spares.

Fig. 6

COTTER

SHEAR PIN

LUBRICATION PLUG

PROP

compressed explosive mixture. Ignited by the spark plug, it burns with a roaring flame. Up go temperature and pressure, forcing the piston down on its power stroke. So far, internal cylinder dynamics are the same as in the four-stroke engine.

Well down on power stroke and approaching bottom center, the piston's crown uncovers a port in one side of the cylinder. This is the exhaust port, and out through it rush the hot, burned products of combustion. The combination power-exhaust stroke has performed its function.

Numerous outboard malfunctions are traceable to the power-exhaust stroke: If the spark plug is dirty or fouled with soot, it can't start the internal fire and the engine remains dead. If spark timing is too early the engine remains dead. If ignition is late, the mixture may not ignite, or, if it does, power will be lost and the engine may pop back and spit. If the exhaust port is partially clogged, engine power will suffer. And so it goes.

Intake-Compression: Intake, inlet, induction, call it what you like: it's much different in the outboard.

Late in the power stroke, you'll remember, the piston uncovered the exhaust port. Continuing its downward travel, it then uncovers an inlet port on the other side of the cylinder from the exhaust. Behind the port lurks mixture under moderate pressure and, of course, its pressure shoves it into the cylinder. While rushing into the cylinder, the fresh gasoline/air mixture pushes out more of the exhaust products, aiding in the scavenging of the cylinder, and making room for the fresh charge.

"What," you ask, "creates that pressure to push the fresh charge into the cylinder?"

It comes from crankcase compression, pressure indigenous to the two-stroke motor, unknown in the four-stroke machine. In the outboard, each piston, con-rod, and small length of crankshaft is sealed off, in a confined space. Naturally, as the piston rises and falls, this space gets bigger and smaller; its volume changes, therefore so does its pressure. When the piston descends on power-exhaust stroke, it compresses the contents of its individual crankcase. That's where the pressure originates, driving the mixture into the cylinder. Consequently, when the port is uncovered by the piston, *whoosh* goes the

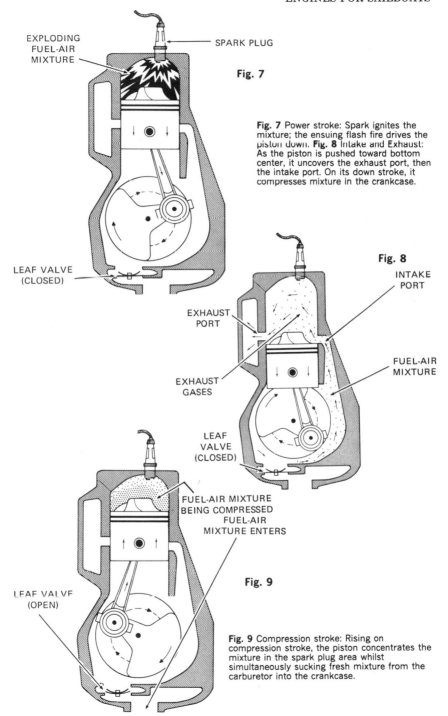

EXPLODING
FUEL-AIR
MIXTURE

SPARK PLUG

Fig. 7

Fig. 7 Power stroke: Spark ignites the mixture; the ensuing flash fire drives the piston down. **Fig. 8** Intake and Exhaust: As the piston is pushed toward bottom center, it uncovers the exhaust port, then the intake port. On its down stroke, it compresses mixture in the crankcase.

LEAF VALVE
(CLOSED)

Fig. 8

INTAKE
PORT

EXHAUST
PORT

FUEL-AIR
MIXTURE

EXHAUST
GASES

LEAF
VALVE
(CLOSED)

FUEL-AIR MIXTURE
BEING COMPRESSED
FUEL-AIR
MIXTURE ENTERS

Fig. 9

LEAF VALVE
(OPEN)

Fig. 9 Compression stroke: Rising on compression stroke, the piston concentrates the mixture in the spark plug area whilst simultaneously sucking fresh mixture from the carburetor into the crankcase.

37

mixture into the cylinder.

How does mixture get into the crankcase? Through a short intake manifold, the carburetor is ducted into the crankcase, not the cylinder. When the piston rises, a partial vacuum is created in the crankcase. This sucks mixture from the carb into the crankcase. During power stroke, the piston compresses the mix in the case, readying it for induction. It cannot be blown back through the carburetor because there's an automatic check valve (reed valve) between crankcase and carb.

Meanwhile, back in the cylinder proper, mixture has been pushed into the space. The piston rises, covering first the intake port, then the exhaust. Compression commences; mixture is compressed into the combustion chamber; spark snaps, and the cycle is repeated.

Many outboard troubles originate during the intake-compression stroke. Considerable outboard crankiness springs from malfunctions in the induction and crankcase compression systems. Reed valves stick or break, preventing the engine from breathing. The crankcase becomes flooded with gasoline, drenching the spark plug and drowning the spark. Alternately, the carburetor starves the crankcase, making the mixture too weak to burn. Then the engine dies.

Outboard Lubrication: We left this to last because until you understand about crankcase induction and compression, the lubrication business would sound like Greek.

Obviously, in a crankcase through which gasoline and air flow in a fast, pulsating stream, you can't also have a reserve of lubricating oil. It'd be blown into the cylinder and burned along with the combustible mixture. Therefore, in the outboard a small quantity of oil is mixed with the gasoline. As oil-bearing fuel is carried through the crankcase, it lubricates bearings and piston walls. Completing its job, it finds its way into the cylinder and is burned along with the fuel. That's why outboards have that characteristic smell and telltale wisp of blue smoke trailing behind.

The only drawbacks to the fuel-in-gasoline lubrication system are the smell and trace of smoke. It's simple and effective: As long as you remember to add oil (about a pint in 6 gallons of gasoline) the system will work fine, giving little trouble. Should you forget to add oil, the engine may ultimately be shredded; at the least, it will be damaged.

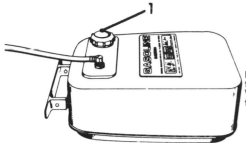

Fig. 10 Chrysler portable outboard motor fuel tank has a vent screw in the filler cap. Vent must be opened to prevent motor from starving due to air lock.

If you skimp on oil, motor parts will wear too fast. Should you mix in too much oil, you'll foul the spark plugs, making the engine a brat to start. You'll also increase the smoke and smell emanating from the exhaust. In a following wind, this can dull the romance of an otherwise beautiful passage.

The outboard lower unit is lubricated separately with viscous oil which is replaced once a season. If you forget to have the lower unit serviced occasionally, it'll finally rust and the rig will quit working.

V

Understanding Ignition

In previous chapters we nonchalantly tossed off such expressions as, ". . . the spark zapped across the spark plug gap," or ". . . the spark plug ignited the mixture." Well and good when one is working comfortably at his typewriter. But you're a sailor. You know better. Lots of times the spark does not zap, jump, or ignite. It does not do anything, particularly when the weather is wet, the wind is out of the southwest, and you are more than a little interested in clawing off that lee shore under power.

The thrust of this chapter is to introduce you to the innards of the conventional ignition system. The purpose is to help you take care of the thing, nurse it, tune it a little, and get it cooking when it's clammy. In the following chapter, we'll dig deeper into doctoring the ignition; but in the present one we want briefly to discuss each ignition component, see where it fits into the big picture, and consider what kinds of hell it can bring the skipper when it gets sick.

Briefly, then, let's touch bases with the components of the ignition system as found on the inboard auxiliary engine, and consider what sneaky troubles each segment can generate when feeling dank and nasty. In our succinct description, we will start with the ignition key, working our way through to the spark plugs, where the high voltage pays off by igniting the mixture. If you want to sharpen your skills in trouble-shooting your auxiliary's ignition problems, please read this chapter. Later, when we wade in deeper, you'll have a firm grasp on the fundamentals.

Ignition Switch: Customarily located in the cockpit close to the helmsman, the ignition switch completes a circuit between the boat's battery and the ignition system's low voltage sector. Its function is simple, but if its contacts or connections corrode, or if the wires attached to it loosen, the switch will generate all kinds of ignition ailments. An old, corroded switch can cause hard starting, misfiring, stalling and numerous similar troubles, generally blamed on a more exotic component.

Low Voltage Wiring: Called "primary circuit wiring," the conductors in the ignition key circuit are often neglected because they don't seem as critical as those delivering high voltage to the spark plugs. Don't be fooled. If battery voltage wires are allowed to get ratty, ignition performance will suffer, and the spark may quit when one of the wires frays or breaks.

The Ballast: Wired in the conductor between key switch and ignition coil, the ballast, a resistor, prevents the coil from drawing excessive current. When cold, ballast resistance is lower than when hot. This characteristic allows the ignition coil more juice for starting, then drops the amperes for proper running characteristics. On the family car, the ballast resistor seldom misbehaves. But in the damp sailboat environment, it often corrodes; either its innards or its connections rot. Then one of two unpleasant things happen: Either spark intensity is reduced, making the engine balky, or else ignition is killed entirely, with the unhappy result so familiar to all sailors.

(If, despite your best efforts, you can't locate a ballast on your auxiliary, don't stew. Some ignition systems function without any ballast.)

Ignition Coil: It's called a coil; actually it's a transformer with two windings around an iron core. The primary or low-voltage winding comprises a few dozen turns of heavy, insulated magnet wire and has a resistance of maybe five ohms. This is the winding which carries battery voltage.

The secondary winding inside the ignition coil is a cat of a different stripe. Thousands of turns of fine magnet wire characterize the secondary. Wound around the same core as the primary, it carries the high voltage that generates snap in the spark plugs, and its resistance is on the order of 10,000 ohms. In the marine environment, the principal troubles with ignition coils spring from dampness worming its way into the works: Once the assembly gets wet inside, it corrodes, short-circuits the spark; and kills the engine. Another trouble is

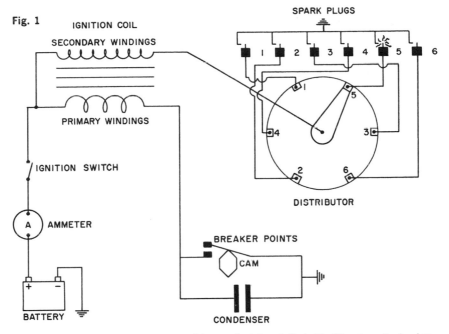

Fig. 1 The basic ignition system is not terribly complicated, as indicated by this schematic showing its components.

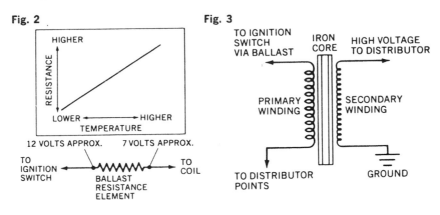

Fig. 2 When cold, the ballast resistor conducts almost full battery voltage to the coil; but when warmed, it drops potential to approximately 7 volts. Keep this in mind when measuring the voltage at the coil's terminals. **Fig. 3** The ignition "coil" is really a transformer. Low voltage flows in the primary; hot spark voltage flows in the secondary. **Fig. 4** High voltage wire is insulated by the coil's tower of plastic. Hairline cracks in the tower will destroy ignition performance.

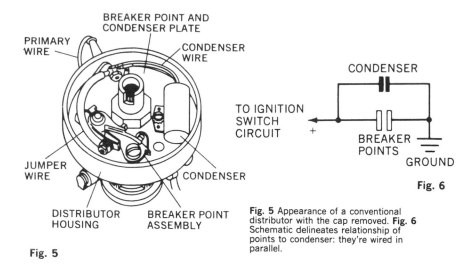

BREAKER POINT AND
CONDENSER PLATE

PRIMARY
WIRE

CONDENSER
WIRE

CONDENSER

TO IGNITION
SWITCH
CIRCUIT

BREAKER
POINTS

GROUND

Fig. 6

JUMPER
WIRE

CONDENSER

DISTRIBUTOR
HOUSING

BREAKER POINT
ASSEMBLY

Fig. 5

Fig. 5 Appearance of a conventional distributor with the cap removed. **Fig. 6** Schematic delineates relationship of points to condenser: they're wired in parallel.

hairline cracking of the plastic part carrying the hot wire which runs to the distributor. This is sometimes called the coil's *tower*. When hairline cracks hold moisture, they become conductors, grounding out high potential and killing spark.

You'll see three electrical connections to the coil assembly. The heavily coated wire emerging from the insulated tower is the high-voltage lead conducting spark to the distributor. One of the smaller diameter low voltage wires brings battery current from the ignition key, and the other low voltage wire runs to the breaker points inside the distributor.

The Distributor: Here's the heart of ignition and the source of countless ills. There are several separate functions all going on in the same enclosure called the distributor. Inside, spark is timed and distributed to the correct plug at the appropriate time. Performing this job is a set of points, condenser, rotor, distributor cap, and automatic advance. Working as a team, these parts function as follows:

Points: How many times have you heard someone say, "The engine won't run because the points are bad." Just what are points, anyway?

The points are a low-voltage switch in the ignition coil's primary circuit. They're in series with the coil. When they open, they break

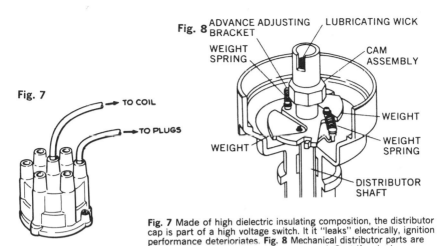

Fig. 8 ADVANCE ADJUSTING BRACKET

LUBRICATING WICK

WEIGHT SPRING

CAM ASSEMBLY

WEIGHT

WEIGHT SPRING

WEIGHT

DISTRIBUTOR SHAFT

Fig. 7

→ TO COIL

→ TO PLUGS

Fig. 7 Made of high dielectric insulating composition, the distributor cap is part of a high voltage switch. It it "leaks" electrically, ignition performance deteriorates. **Fig. 8** Mechanical distributor parts are shown with points and condenser removed. Centrifugal advance weights and springs can be seen.

the circuit; that's when spark occurs (not when they close). In brief, the points are a timing switch, opening and closing each time a piston reaches top center and requires spark.

Every kind of ignition trouble has its origin in the points: Improper timing, weak spark, no spark, early spark, late spark, anemic spark. You name it; and in the next chapter we'll see how to tame it.

Condenser: Many engineers refer to the condenser as a *capacitor.* It's the same animal, but we'll stick to the old term so as not to confuse the ordinary condenser with a similar component used in modern capacitor-discharge transistorized ignition.

Usually located inside the distributor, the condenser is wired or shunted directly across the points. Its function is spooky. Engineers say that *it provides a low impedance path for surge current.* Or they'll intone, "It causes the ignition coil's primary winding to electrically 'ring.'" So it does. But the main consideration of interest to the sailor is that if it is defective, there's no spark. The condenser is pretty much an all-or-nothing kind of gimmick: It either functions well, or it's deader than a stone. Seldom is it intermittent. In the following chapter, we'll see how to check a condenser.

Rotor: The center vertical shaft inside the distributor spins around at half engine speed when the engine is running. At its top end there's an insulated arm spinning with it. The arm carries a metal contact which rotates inside the distributor cap, acting as a rotary switch. The rotary switch distributes timed ignition pulses to the right spark plug wires at the appropriate instant. That's the theory. But the rotor can also be a source of trouble. If it gets dirty or damp, it can drown out the high voltage it is supposed to distribute. Then the engine mysteriously dies, and, alas, no one knows what happened to that hot spark which left the coil and entered the distributor.

Distributor Cap: It looks like a capitol dome with a group of heavy wires sprouting skyward. The distributor cap is a heavy insulator and comprises part of the switch to which the rotor distributes spark. Its inside contacts receive high voltage blips of spark from the rotor, distributing them to the spark plug wires in correct order. Fair enough. But the distributor cap can cause some of the most difficult ignition troubles in the book, ones tough to diagnose. Dampness inside the cap will invisibly ground the hottest spark. Moisture on its outside will do the same. Worse, invisible hairline cracks in its inner or outer surface will spawn high-voltage leaks which either deteriorate engine performance or kill it altogether. Although the distributor cap appears to be a quiescent, static component, its role in engine performance is important, and must not be neglected in maintenance and trouble-shooting schedules.

Automatic Advance: Hidden in the bowels of the distributor housing lies a set of weights spinning with the center shaft. Centrifugal force throws these weights out radially away from the center as the engine spins faster, pressing them against the restraint of attached springs. As the weights fly farther out, their angular position moves forward the cam which actuates the breaker points. This makes the spark occur earlier in the cycle, "advancing the spark," as mechanics say. If the spark is not advanced (made to happen earlier), the engine will be sluggish at higher speeds, will use too much gasoline, and may bark back through its carburetor.

Automatic advance devices seldom give the family automobile engine any trouble. But in the auxiliary engine, they sometimes rust. Then they stick, fail to do their job, and make the sailor's life miserable.

High-Voltage Wiring: Those wires running between distributor and spark plugs and from ignition coil to distributor carry high voltage, often in excess of 12,000 volts. They are an important part of the ignition picture, subject to numerous ills. If they are not dressed properly, the engine may misfire; when they're wet, it may stop; if they grow old and neglected, they may interfere with decent engine performance. Like other ignition components, they've got to be cared for.

Spark Plugs: Possibly the simplest component in the ignition system, spark plugs are at the payoff end of the line. If they don't function well, the hottest spark voltage in the world is lost. The spark plug is simply a center porcelain insulator fitted into a metal bushing screwed into the cylinder's combustion compartment. Through the center of the porcelain runs a heavy wire conductor carrying the high voltage. At the end of the plug, inside the cylinder, the center electrode is set close to a side electrode attached or "grounded" to the cylinder head. Spark voltage is delivered to the center conductor; inside the cylinder, spark jumps across a gap space to the other electrode. In doing so, it ignites the mixture in the cylinder.

Though the spark plug is simple, it can louse up engine performance in numerous ways. If its center porcelain develops a crack, even an invisible one, the high voltage is "grounded" and the plug cannot fire its cylinder. Should the plug get drenched, it will not work. When soot or carbon builds up on the portion of the plug inside the cylinder, its electrodes are short circuited, and the plug is as dead as a flounder. Plugs must be serviced. They must be replaced periodically.

How Ignition Parts Function Together

Assume that the ignition switch is closed and the engine is standing still—something it does without a flaw. Further assume that the distributor points are closed; they're touching each other, making contact. The stage is now set, and current flows through the ignition system's primary circuit from the battery through the ignition switch and ballast, through the ignition coil's primary winding, through the distributor points and then back to the battery via something mysteriously called "ground."

Let's stop right there. How can you have "ground" on a floating boat?

"Ground," when used in connection with marine engine electricity, refers to the heavy metal of the engine head, block, and metal accessories, all of which are mechanically and electrically connected. They are electric current-carrying parts in this ground arrangement, and one of the storage battery terminals, the negative one, is attached to the pseudo-ground. One terminal of the spark plugs, starter, alternator, and distributor is attached to ground, which serves as one conductor, the negative conductor, returning current to the battery.

In the distributor, one ignition point is connected to the battery through the coil, ballast and key switch. That's the positive or hot point. The other point is connected to ground. When the points close, a circuit is completed through them from hot to ground.

With the points closed and current flowing through the coil's primary winding, a magnetic field is built up inside the coil, around its iron core. The stage is now set for some action.

The action takes place when the engine rotates. As it does so, a little vertical cam shaft in the center of the distributor rotates at half engine speed. Lobes or raised segments on the rotating shaft open and close the points. Each time an engine piston reaches close to top center, a lobe bumps open the points. Immediately the points open, current ceases flowing in the ignition coil's primary winding, causing the electromagnetic field to collapse. In collapsing, it induces extremely high voltage in the secondary winding. This is spark voltage.

Earlier, we mentioned that a condenser is connected across the points. When the point set is closed, the condenser is discharged; it is inactive. Immediately that the points open, the condenser is hit with a pulse of voltage from the coil's primary. Acting like an electrical spring, the condenser causes current to flow back and forth rapidly between itself and the coil, and this "ringing" action builds up the spark's intensity.

Leaving the coil's secondary winding, hot spark voltage travels out of the tower, through a high-voltage wire to the distributor cap. Inside the distributor, it enters the center contact on the rotor arm. As the arm spins around, it distributes the spark to the connection for the correct cylinder. Think of the rotor and cap as a rotary sequence switch, selecting the correct spark plug to fire at an appropriate time.

Out from the distributor cap via high-voltage wires goes the spark to the spark plugs. They're the end of the line. The payoff. Inside the cylinder, high voltage snaps across the small gap from the plug's center to its ground electrode. In doing so, it ignites the surrounding combustible mixture; and that's what it's supposed to do.

Ignition timing is correct when the points open and close in correct synchronization with piston rhythm. Each time a piston approaches top center on compression, the points must open, initiating spark.

"Initial" timing is determined by the rotational position of the distributor in its boss. Initial timing is that when the engine is rotating slowly. "Power" timing is determined by the centrifugal advance mechanism which steps the timing forward as the engine speeds up. Typical initial timing might be top dead center. Then, when the centrifugal advance does its work at higher speed, timing might be advanced to 25° before top center.

The distance which points open and close (called clearance) is adjustable and has a considerable effect on timing and general engine performance. Typical clearance is on the order of 0.015″, measured with a feeler gauge, a strip of metal of accurately known thickness. "Dwell" is the percentage of time or number of rotational degrees which the points remain closed, and is effected by clearance adjustment. Measured by electrical instruments, typical dwell for a four- or six-cylinder engine is on the order of 36°, although some four-cylinder distributors are designed for more dwell. Proper clearance, timing, and dwell are given in the technical manual available with any engine.

That owner's or shop manual: You must have it to properly take care of the auxiliary. If you are serious about keeping the old teapot running, treasure that book. If you have lost it, or never got one, make a good try at getting one from the manufacturer. Write for it. Offer to pay. Without the good book, you're floundering; you don't know whether to leave the marks to starboard or port.

VI

Tuning
the Ignition

Since the main thrust of this book is toward keeping your auxiliary running and keeping you out of trouble, you may wonder why we have a chapter devoted to "tuning." After all, you're not trying to race the boat under power, you simply want the auxiliary to give you as little concern as possible. "Why not give us trouble-shooting information before bothering with tuning?" could be your legitimate beef.

The dope on tuning comes first for two reasons: First, if you keep the engine reasonably well tuned, it is far less likely to require trouble-shooting. Second, if you understand how to tune it, the iron breeze and its ignition become less of a mystery, therefore much easier to doctor.

Admit it now: you'll spend days tuning the standing rigging on your yacht, correct? Then why not spend a few hours tuning the auxiliary's ignition system? If that conglomerate of components is happy and secure, you're almost home free as far as engine troubles are concerned, because most basic engine troubles spring from the ignition system.

Tuning is more than a matter of making screwdriver adjustments on diverse electrical components. It includes simple operations such as inspecting and tightening connections as well as making sure components are lubricated. With that thought in mind, here is a suggested tune-up program for your auxiliary's ignition:

Start with the battery, working all the way through to the spark plugs.

Inspect all connections to the storage battery, making sure they are clean and tight. An intermittent contact here can cause missing, particularly when the boat is yawing and pitching, perhaps even pounding into a sea. Motion can make poor connections erratic, causing the ignition to falter just when you need it most.

Trace all wires leading to the ignition switch, making sure they're well secured and free of frayed spots. If you locate wires which are loose and dangling, secure them neatly, making sure your method of attachment does not chafe their insulation. Where you support the conductors, use a soft rubber ferrule or insulated clip.

Inspect and tighten all connections to the ignition switch. Rub some Vaseline petroleum jelly on the ignition key, then insert and withdraw the key several times to lubricate the lock. If its insides corrode badly, it may cease to function. A hint: When leaving your boat, plaster a short length of Scotch tape over the lock's opening. This'll keep water out.

While you are fussing about in back of the instrument panel, tighten up on all other electrical connections. Be careful. Don't short circuit any terminals with your tools, making a shower of sparks. If you want to be on the safe side, disconnect the positive storage battery cable before messing with the exposed connections.

Trace the wires running from ignition switch to ballast resistor. Secure them if they flap loose.

As noted above, don't be disturbed if you don't find a ballast. Some systems have none, per se. In place of a ballast resistor, resistance wire is used: a section of the wire in the primary circuit is alloy rather than copper. Its resistance is sufficient to do the job, and no separate component is seen. Another approach is for the manufacturer to include the ballast inside the ignition coil. As we said, don't fret if you can't find a ballast.

Assume you do find it. Tighten its connections. Inspect visually, looking for corrosion. Should your glance be rewarded with a wad of corrosion, replace the ballast. If that corrosion continues doing its dirty work, the unit will lose all continuity, and ignition will fall on its face.

Now to the ignition coil: Assure yourself that it is securely mounted. If it rattles, it may chafe through and destroy itself. Inspect and tighten the low voltage (battery circuit) wires attached to the coil. Intermittent bad connections here will make the engine miss, cough, sputter, and run rotten.

Pull the high voltage wire from the coil's tower. Look for corrosion. Clean the wire terminal and the copper receptacle inside the tower. The receptacle can be cleaned with a Q-tip or other cotton swab dipped in a little lacquer thinner. If there's lots of green corrosion inside, roll up some fine sandpaper and clean out the hole. It's good to do this once a year, because if corrosion builds up in this friction-fit connection, spark may be strangled even before it can leap from the coil. We have seen this happen on several sailboats.

Wipe off the coil's entire exterior, paying extra attention to the tower. When it's clean and dry, spray it with a mist of CRC. I don't know the composition of CRC, it's some kind of patented mouse-milk, but I use it regularly and think it's a great moisture fighter around auxiliary engines. I own no stock in the company making it, but you can buy it in marine stores and hardwares, and I recommend that you keep a can in your spare-parts box. I do.

The reason for cleaning, drying, and spraying the coil with CRC is this: When dry, the coil may behave beautifully, even if it's dirty. But when the weather gets drizzly and dank, dirt on the coil's tower holds miniscule droplets of water. These comprise a conductive surface over which spark voltage can find its way to ground. In that case, the spark plugs are starved and, of course, the engine remains deader than driftwood.

Before removing high-voltage wires from the distributor cap, label each wire with a little marker or piece of tape, noting which position each assumes on the distributor. If you fail to do so, you may wind up with a handful of ignition wires, wondering which wire belongs in what position. Should you attach spark plug wires incorrectly on the distributor cap, either the engine won't run, or will run horribly.

One at a time, pull each spark plug wire from its receptacle in the distributor cap. Clean the terminals on the wire's bitter ends and clean the metal inserts inside the receptacles. Use the same procedure that you did on the ignition coil tower. With a clean, dry cloth or some paper towels, clean the cap's exterior. After giving it a good buff, spray it with a mist of CRC, wiping off the excess. This elementary treatment may save you a lot of swearing some bleak, damp morning.

Remove the distributor cap. Tilt it up so you can look inside. If the little metal contacts (one for each spark plug) appear corroded, pitted, or burned, its a good idea to replace the cap. A new one costs but a few dollars. Mop out the inside of the cap, give it a light, misty spray of moisture inhibitor. Wipe out any excess.

Inside the distributor, you'll see the rotor. If its metal parts appear burned, corroded, or otherwise less than Bristol trim, replace it. Wipe it clean; spray it. If this little voltage-carrying gizmo is electrically leaky, it will kill the engine, and in trouble-shooting you will have a devil of a time finding the buried trouble.

Delve farther down into the distributor and you'll find the point set, that magic timing switch. Now is the time for decision: Shall you mess with them or not? If you have but few tools, and those of the monkey-wrench variety, leave the points alone. But if you've a reasonable set of small tools (screwdrivers, small pliers and wrenches) go ahead. You are dexterous enough to handle a spinnaker, so you are capable of tackling a set of ignition points. The only somewhat special tool you'll need is a feeler gauge set. Housed inside a metal handle that looks somewhat like a penknife, a good set of feeler gauges costs about three dollars. Tell the fellow in an automobile parts store that you want a set of feeler gauges for ignition work. You can use them on spark plugs, too. While you're in the store, spend another three dollars buying a set of ignition wrenches. They're fine for use on all kinds of small nuts and bolts, not only those on the ignition system.

Open the points. With your finger or a small tool, separate them and inspect their contacting surfaces. If those mating faces are quite smooth, you're home free. But if they're pitted, burned, and irregular like the moon's surface, the best thing you can do is replace the point set. In fact, if there's any doubt in your mind, replace the points. They're critical to good ignition, yet cost but two or three dollars per set. Since you have gone to this much trouble, why not go the whole route and renew? Don't be penny wise.

Study how the points are installed in the distributor, then carefully remove them, using your small tools. Taking out the old set is no great production. Replace with a fresh set, installing them mechanically and electrically in the same manner as the old. Now you are

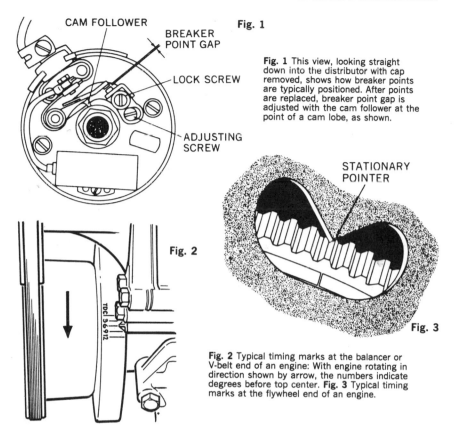

Fig. 1

CAM FOLLOWER

BREAKER
POINT GAP

LOCK SCREW

ADJUSTING
SCREW

Fig. 1 This view, looking straight down into the distributor with cap removed, shows how breaker points are typically positioned. After points are replaced, breaker point gap is adjusted with the cam follower at the point of a cam lobe, as shown.

STATIONARY
POINTER

Fig. 2

Fig. 3

Fig. 2 Typical timing marks at the balancer or V-belt end of an engine: With engine rotating in direction shown by arrow, the numbers indicate degrees before top center. **Fig. 3** Typical timing marks at the flywheel end of an engine.

ready to adjust their clearance, wherein accuracy is important.

Proceed as follows:

Gingerly crank the engine, rotating it a few degrees at a time. This maneuver is easiest if you remove all the spark plugs first. The engine can be turned manually by hand crank, exposed flywheel, pulley, or V-belt. Alternately, it can be jogged with the electric starter. Jiggle the engine around until the little rubbing block on the moving ignition point is exactly at the top of a cam lobe. In other words, the points are as wide apart as the cam can urge them.

Now, adjust the distance between the point contacts to the clearance specified by the engine manual. Use your feeler gauge to measure this clearance; then tighten the set screw. Rotate the engine a revolution or so; then measure the clearance again, making sure you're close to the exact specification. That's all there is to it.

Close-hauled, when you change the trim of a sail, you have to change heading slightly to keep her from luffing or being too broad on the wind. So with the distributor. If you alter point clearance, even slightly, you must re-time the engine. "Timing" an engine sounds forbidding, but it's really like shooting fish in a barrel. Try it.

Consult the good book, getting the recommended initial timing. Chances are it'll be within a few degrees of top dead center. Find the timing marks on flywheel or balancer wheel; that's the wheel at one end of the engine, carrying the V-belt for necessary drives. Now, in tiny increments, tickle the engine over, rotating it until the points *just barely* start to open. At this juncture, the stationary timing pointer and appropriate moving timing mark should line up.

Suppose they don't line up? Now what?

Loosen the nut or machine screw holding the distributor down in its mount. Ever so slightly rotate the distributor in either direction. Tighten the holding screw, then crank the engine over a revolution and try the timing again. If it's worse, you rotated the distributor in the wrong direction. Loosen the screw, rotate it the other direction; tighten the screw and try the timing again. Continue the trial and error bit until the timing suits you.

You can eliminate the ambiguity as to whether clockwise or anti-clockwise distributor rotation advances or retards the timing: Crank the engine in its normal direction of rotation. Watch which way the distributor rotor turns. Knowing the direction of rotor rotation, you can apply the following simple rules:

1. Shifting the distributor body in the direction of rotor rotation retards the timing, making it later.

2. Shifting the distributor body against the direction of rotor rotation advances the timing, making it earlier.

How can you determine when the points *just barely* open? Several methods are popular:

• Insert a very thin strip of plastic (the gossamer type used to wrap food) between the points. Keep modest finger tension on the strip. When the points "break," the strip will be released.

• Connect a 12-volt test light electrically across the points. Turn on

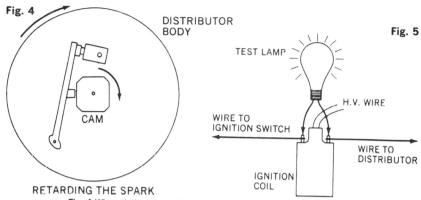

Fig. 4 When timing the engine, rotate the distributor body in the same direction as cam rotation to retard the spark. **Fig. 5** Using a static timing light: When the points open, the light will glow.

the ignition key. When the points separate, the light will start to glow.

• Connect a voltmeter or test light across the two low-voltage terminals on the ignition coil. Turn on the ignition key. When the points break, the test light will extinguish or the meter will show no voltage. The same kind of indication can be gotten from an ammeter in *series* with either of the low voltage coil connections.

When you're satisfied that the initial timing is on the nose, turn your attention to the high-voltage wires which connect coil to distributor and distributor to spark plugs. These are the spinal cords of the ignition system; unless they're in prime health, the motor is going to misbehave in damp weather. It'll do worse than misbehave. It won't start.

Inspect the high-voltage insulation on those wires. The rubber composition must be clean, resilient, fresh, and free of minute cracks or checks. If the wiring appears less than perfect, if it is several seasons old, if it looks weathered and scaly, by all means replace it. Surface imperfections absorb salt and moisture, becoming conductive canals which drown out the spark, making the engine a rotter to live with.

After replacing the high-voltage wires, dress them neatly, making straight runs where possible. Avoid bunching the wires; don't run them through conduit. Do keep them apart with air spacing between, and arrange to have them touch as little metal as possible.

Wipe the high voltage wires with a clean cloth or dry paper towel. Spray them with a mist of CRC. Don't be tempted to lacquer them or paint them with insulating varnish. We've seen this done. Looks magnificent when you first apply the dope. But then the pigments harden, the surface cracks, absorbs water, and kills the ignition.

The hottest, best-timed ignition pulse is wasted on a sick spark plug. If the plug is dirty, foul, sooty, badly adjusted or wet, it will drown the high voltage. It's important, then, that in your tuning endeavors you manicure the spark plugs.

Before removing the plugs, blow away any dirt hiding in the plug recesses; you don't want it in the cylinders. Unscrew the plugs and have a look. If the business end of each plug appears almost like new, simply showing the effects of heat, you can set the gap, and re-install. But if you've any doubt, by all means replace the entire set of plugs. They're important, and not that expensive.

Three things to do when installing new plugs: 1. Make sure the new ones are the correct type. 2. Adjust the gap to recommended clearance. 3. See that there is a fresh washer on the plug (unless it's the tapered-seat variety) and screw it to the correct tightness.

Gap is the distance between the two electrodes across which the spark jumps. Adjust it by moving the side electrode slightly until the correct feeler gauge blade just slips in between the two. Don't try to bend the middle electrode lest you break the porcelain. If, despite your best efforts you cannot find the gap specification for your engine, set the plug gaps at 0.028".

According to Hoyle, you really should tighten the plugs to specification using a torque wrench. If you have a torque wrench, or can borrow one, go by the good book. However, chances are that you don't have that special tool; so you'll have to use your judgement. 25 pound-feet of torque is a typical tightness. That's 25 pounds of pull at the end of a wrench handle one foot long. Try to estimate that torque when replacing plugs. Don't get too enthusiastic and lay on the wrench as though it were the tiller on a catboat carrying a bad weather helm. You might strip the threads.

Be sure to connect the right plug wires to the appropriate plugs.

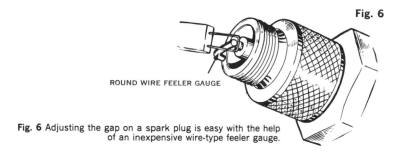

Fig. 6

ROUND WIRE FEELER GAUGE

Fig. 6 Adjusting the gap on a spark plug is easy with the help of an inexpensive wire-type feeler gauge.

Should you interchange some wires inadvertently, the engine will bark and spit at you. But it won't work worth a tinker's damn.

You're finished tuning the engine, and it seems to run well. Now there's a useful experiment you can perform, and it may make the machine a mite more reliable as a crew member.

Some dark night, preferably when it's dank and wet, watch the engine perform in the dark. The blacker it is, the better. Entomb yourself with the running engine, watching the ignition coil, wires, distributor, and plugs. Look for telltale blips of blue spark, Saint Elmo's fire, tiny fireflies of wild electrons around the high-voltage components. Those tiny lightning flashes are wasted spark. They signal that the system is leaky and needs attention. They warn that damp morning starts are going to be a clambake. Take heed, captain, and clean up the leaks. Literally: Renew wiring, clean and dry components, wipe things dry, then spray with moisture inhibitor.

Now try again. When high-potential components are trimmed Bristol fashion, they'll be invisible in the dark, even in the damp, troll-infested opacity indigenous to the sailboat bilge.

Ignition Tuning Epilogue

What follows in this chapter is a deeper look into ignition tuning, and some sailors may want to skip on to the next chapter unless they're interested in assorted fine points of the art.

If you don't have the technical manual applying to your engine, you must estimate both point clearance and timing. These guesstimates you can make just as intelligently as deciding when to break tacks and make for the windward mark.

Estimating Point Clearance: Simply elect to use a clearance of 0.015", and the engine will probably tick along just as happy as a clam. Certainly, in a pinch, fifteen-thousandths is a happy compromise clearance.

If you'd like to get a little more scientific, try this tack:

1. Delicately rotate the engine until the breaker point cam follower is centered in a *flat* between two cam lobes (high places). The points are closed.

2. Now, adjust the points to precisely zero clearance. The contact surfaces are just touching each other, and the cam follower or rubbing block is also resting in the flat.

3. Next, rotate the engine until the points are wide open: The points are now at maximum clearance. Using a feeler gauge, measure this clearance. On a typical 4-cylinder engine it might be 0.030".

4. Half of that maximum opening is estimated proper point clearance for your engine. The chances are a hundred to one that your auxiliary will be perfectly happy with a point clearance determined by this method. After all, you're tuning for reliability, not to enter a powerboat sweepstakes.

Estimating Initial Timing: Don't sweat too much if you can't find any published information regarding initial timing on your mill. Just assume that it's exactly top dead center, and set up the engine with that timing. When you're ready, operate the auxiliary; let your feel and ear tell you if the timing is about right.

Start the engine and warm it. Set it at idle. With top-dead-center timing, it should idle smoothly, at least from the ignition standpoint. Take the boat to open water and advance the throttle to cruising speed. Should the response seem dull, if the engine hesitates, balks, perhaps pops back through the carburetor, try advancing the timing. Rotate the distributor body slightly *opposite* the direction of rotor rotation.

Advancing the spark will pep up the engine and should improve general performance. But don't overdo it. Too much advance is hard on the machine, may cause it to knock when working hard, and will make it idle rough, though fast.

Playing a little with the timing and using your ear, you should be able to hit the nicest tune. You'll probably find the best compromise somewhere between top dead center and 8° before top center. And

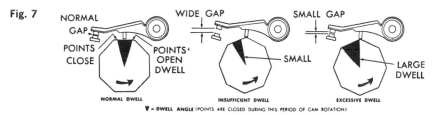

Fig. 7 Sketch shows how point dwell angle effects point gap or clearance.

don't fret much if you think you're a hair off. It won't hurt the machine.

What is Dwell? You've heard mechanics use the term; stinkpotters talk about it a lot. Dwell is the number of degrees during which the points remain or dwell together, conducting current through the coil's primary. Dwell is another way of expressing point clearance: Less clearance results in more dwell; more clearance results in less dwell.

We avoided a discussion of dwell in the heart of this chapter because, for an auxiliary engine, if you adjust the point clearance accurately, the dwell will be close enough. Tuners of racing and high performance engines stew around about dwell considerably, but don't worry too much about it in your auxiliary's distributor.

Now that we have depreciated dwell, we'll tell how to measure it, should you be inclined.

Beg, buy, or borrow a dwell meter. Connect it according to its individual directions. (The Heathkit meter, for example, simply clips onto the two low voltage terminals on the ignition coil.) Idle the engine, watching the meter. It will indicate the dwell.

Fair enough. However, supposing the points are adjusted according to specification but the dwell falls outside of specified limits? What should you do? Re-adjust the point clearance so that the dwell comes into spec. Let the clearance fall where it may. Typical specifications on dwell are 30° for eight-cylinder engines, 36° to 40° for six-cylinder engines, and 38° to 50° for four-cylinder motors.

Power Timing: We have described how you go about adjusting initial timing, working on the quiescent engine. With the proper instrument, you can confirm the timing while the engine runs, and happily this operation will also test whether or not the automatic advance is working.

You need a timing light for power timing. Correctly attached to the ignition, this light flashes brightly each time spark plug number one fires. Plug No. 1 is the one farthest from the flywheel. In a subdued light, when you point the strobe light at the timing marks, engine running, the light will "stop" the motion, letting you observe the timing.

At idle, the strobe light should reveal the timing marks in approximately the same relative position as they appeared while the engine was sitting still and you timed it initially. If there's any substantial difference, you can accept the timing light's verdict, and correct the timing. Rotate distributor body *with* rotor rotation to retard; rotate *against* rotation to advance.

Accelerate the engine. As its revolutions increase, approaching usual cruising speed, ignition timing should advance. As you watch the marks under the blinking light of the strobe, the line on the moving part, flywheel or balancer, appears to move against the direction of rotation. Apparent change in angular position indicates that the automatic advance is functioning properly.

Should the timing light tell you that the automatic advance is not functioning, you must have the distributor doctored in an ignition shop. Alternatively, replace it. Lack of advance with increasing rpm. makes the engine sluggish, hurts the exhaust valves, wastes gasoline, leads to overheating, and may induce popping or barking out of the carburetor, particularly when the engine is cool.

In a seldom-used auxiliary, lack of advance is usually caused by rusting of the governor weights. The weights are located in the bottom of the distributor, usually underneath the plate carrying the breaker points. Should your spark fail to advance when tested by a timing light, you might squirt penetrating oil into the area of the weights. The thin oil may free up the mechanism, saving you the chore of taking the distributor to a shop, or of having a mechanic come aboard to doctor the wayward component.

VII

Trouble-Shooting
the Ignition

Before rambling through this chapter of ignition horrors, please read the two preceding chapters, the ones on ignition principles and tuning. Those chapters should give you a good priming, preparing you to tackle trouble-shooting concepts with a sound understanding of what makes things tick.

Engine Cranks But Won't Start

This is probably the most common sailboat auxiliary engine problem known to the unhappy sailor.

First, stop using the starter. Extended periods of cranking will simply drain the battery and are murder on the starter motor. Second, make sure the carburetor is getting gasoline and that it is not flooded. (We'll treat fuel system problems in Chapter X.) Make sure the ignition switch is turned on. Then proceed as follows:

1. Disconnect one of the spark plug wires from a spark plug. Hold the hot end of the wire about a quarter-inch from the engine head or block. Crank the engine a few revolutions with the starter. Spark should jump from the wire's end to engine metal. Assume that it does, and you see hot spark. Then the trouble may be in the plugs.

2. Remove all the spark plugs. Clean and dry them inside and out. Using a propane torch or the galley stove, heat the plugs good and hot, necessitating their being handled with a hot pad like a sizzling frying pan. While the plugs are hot, re-install them. Reconnect the high-voltage wires and give her another try.

Were the plugs soaking wet with gasoline when you removed them? That may indicate that the engine was flooded. Take it easy on that choke. If the engine has an automatic choke, hold it open with your finger while the engine is cranked. This will unflood her.

Were the plugs bone dry when you removed them? If so, the engine may be starved, not getting gasoline. Investigate that route.

But backwater, now, and let's assume that at step No. 1 you observed no spark jumping from the spark plug wire. Then do as follows:

3. Reach for the high-voltage wire connected from ignition coil tower to distributor. Disconnect it at the distributor. Turn on the ignition. Hold the hot end of the wire about a quarter inch from engine metal and crank the engine with the starter a few revolutions. Hot spark should snap from the wire to the engine. If there's no spark, one of the following may be at fault:

a. Defective breaker points

b. Defective condenser

c. Broken wire in the low voltage (primary) circuit

d. Defective ignition coil

e. Open ballast resistor or open ignition switch

Each of these items except the condenser and coil can be checked out as described in the previous chapter. The simplest way to test the coil and condenser is by direct substitution of a known good component. A spare condenser and coil should comprise part of your spare on-board matériel.

Backwater again.

Assume that in step 3 you observed good, hot spark eminating from the ignition coil. Now you've narrowed down the trouble. There's good spark from the coil, but it's not reaching the plugs, therefore it is being lost in the high-voltage wires or distributor. This trouble is not uncommon on damp auxiliary engines. Remove the distributor cap, wipe it bone dry inside and out, spray it with CRC or other moisture inhibitor. Clean and dry the rotor and spray it. Replace the cap; then clean and spray the ignition wires. Spark should now get to the plugs. If not, cap or rotor are defective. Replace both with factory-boxed components; these, too, should be parts among your on-board spares.

Engine Starts but Immediately Quits

The engine fires, runs a few seconds, quits as soon as you release

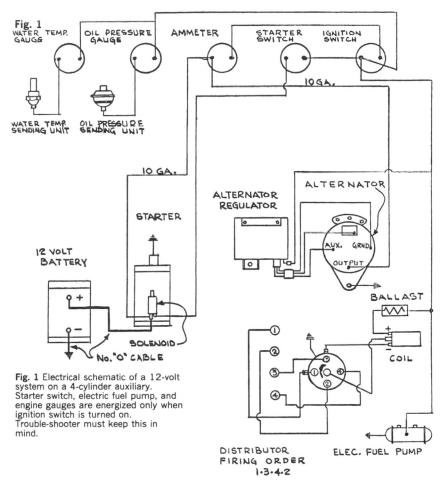

Fig. 1 Electrical schematic of a 12-volt system on a 4-cylinder auxiliary. Starter switch, electric fuel pump, and engine gauges are energized only when ignition switch is turned on. Trouble-shooter must keep this in mind.

the starter switch (which is often combined with the ignition key). This can be a real doozie to trace. However, a likely cause is a break in the wiring between the ballast resistor and coil, or a defective ballast. Here's what happens:

Many engines are fitted with a switch which by-passes or shunts the ballast only when the starter is energized. Often this switch is part of the starter assembly, sometimes it is associated with the ignition switch. While the engine is being cranked, the by-pass switch furnishes full voltage to the coil, eliminating the voltage drop through the ballast. Therefore, if the ballast or its associated wiring opens, the engine sees ignition via the by-pass during the cranking period, but as soon as the starter is released, voltage falls to zero and the engine conks out.

The way to check for this syndrome is to connect a test light from the "Bat" ignition coil terminal to ground. If it glows while the engine is cranked, but extinguishes when cranking ceases, you have nailed down the elusive trouble.

Low-Speed Roughness

Assuming that carburetor low-speed adjustments are well made, overly advanced ignition makes the engine feel "hard" and rough at low speed. Dirty plugs, wet high-voltage wires, and foul breaker points can also make the engine grubby at idle. A damp distributor cap might contribute to the malaise.

Knocking at Advanced Throttle

You shove the throttle forward, pushing your *Mary Anne* against tide and wind. Then, from the engine compartment, you hear that knocking and pinging that sounds as though she swallowed glass marbles. That's detonation. Spark knock. And it signals that spark timing is advanced too far. To correct the condition, which is hard on the engine's internals, retard the spark just sufficiently to eliminate the ping. A better grade of gasoline will help; but these days that's hard to find at the waterfront.

Roughness at All Speeds

Don't confuse this with vibration due to loose engine mounts or simply the coffee pot dancing on the Shipmate stove. We're referring to constant misfiring. Prime suspects are: Cruddy points, dirty or wet wiring, fouled spark plugs, or grossly mistimed ignition. If the roughness has a regular, rhythmic beat, chances are one cylinder is misfiring continually. You can determine which is the guilty cylinder as follows: Using a screwdriver with well-insulated handle, short circuit one plug at a time. When you short circuit a plug which is firing properly, the engine will run rougher than ever. But when you short circuit the plug which is misfiring, the engine will exhibit no change in cadence.

Barking Through the Carburetor

Sometimes even a well-tuned engine will pop or spit back through its air horn (air inlet) when it's cold. But when up to temperature, it should not do so. If the carburetor regularly backfires and barks as you advance the throttle, there's a strong possibility that the ignition is retarded. Advance the timing to recommended setting. If popping and barking persist, the carburetor may be starved for gasoline, the engine may be operating much too cold, or an inlet valve may be burned. Another possibility is that a spark plug may have a chipped porcelain section inside the combustion chamber or all the plugs may be grossly fouled. Before taking a more difficult tack, having the engine seriously doctored, replace the spark plugs.

Engine Quits Suddenly

You're humming along under power; everything is going swimmingly, when suddenly and without warning, she quits dead.

Check the obvious first: Do you have fuel? Is the fuel valve open? Are you sure someone did not bump into the ignition switch inadvertently? Look for obviously broken wires; make sure the engine is not grossly overheated. Try a light or the horn or some other accessory to test if the battery is alive. Then, turn to the ignition, and trouble-shoot it as outlined in the paragraphs under *Engine Cranks but Won't Start.*

This exact trouble pounced upon us once some years ago, and, following our own advice, we attacked the distributor with gusto. Upon opening it we found that the moving ignition point arm, the tiny lever which is pushed open and closed by the distributor cam, was broken in half. Alas, Murphy's Law at work. Fortunately, we carried a spare point set and were able to make repairs and again get under way. When the arm broke, we were off a rotten-looking lee shore, proof that Miller's corollary postulate is almost infallible! If there is any moral to all this, it is: *carry spare parts,* including a set of points.

Performance "Breaks Up" at High Speed

She starts nicely, idles smoothly, performs well up to easy cruising speed. But when you push her hard, she breaks up, loses her grip, misses, acts giddy. You've checked timing, and all seems well in the carburetion and fuel supply department. In that case, there's a distinct possibility that the point clearance is radically misadjusted. Another strong possibility is that the ignition point spring is weak.

We refer to the little leaf spring which urges the moving ignition point to close. If you suspect this trouble, install a new set of points. Point sets are sold complete with fresh springs.

"Tired Blood" Spark

Sometime when you're trouble-shooting, you may observe that the spark is anemic. Rather than jumping across its gap with a hot blue-white snap, having lots of bite, it appears as a thin, weak, stringy line and can't manage to jump more than an eighth inch. Ninety-nine times out of a hundred, this kind of sour spark indicates that the condenser is defective. A fresh replacement condenser should provide the tonic required to fatten the spark and give it the required zap. (There's another component you should include in your parts inventory.)

VIII

Living With a Diesel Aboard

Operating and caring for the diesel is not much different from living with a gasoline inboard auxiliary. Charging, starting, battery, cooling, exhaust, and lubrication systems are pretty much the same as those associated with the gasoline machine. The main difference is that carburetor and electric ignition are replaced by the fuel injection system. Therefore, the thrust of your preventive maintenance is directed toward the fuel system on the diesel, just as it focuses on ignition in the gas burner.

Entrapped air is to the diesel injection system what moisture is to the gas engine's electric ignition: poison. In his instructions, each diesel manufacturer emphasizes: Keep air out of the fuel system. If it *should* sneak into the system (as when you run out of fuel) immediately purge it by bleeding system components. Air trapped in the fuel lines can prevent the diesel from starting, make it run rough, cause it to missfire, make it lose power, and can stop it dead in its tracks while running.

Bleeding the System

Details vary from one engine to another, but the principles of bleeding a fuel system are much the same. The lines, pumps, filters and tubing must each be purged, all the way from fuel tank to injectors. Naturally, when you're indulging in a system-bleeding session, you must have sufficient fuel in the main tank. Otherwise, as you try to pull bubble-free fuel through, you'll suck in more bubbles of air.

The lift pump, an ordinary diaphragm pump drawing fuel from the tank, is fitted with a priming lever on virtually all diesels. The lever allows you to use your finger to operate the pump, forcing fuel through the system while you bleed. The principle is to open vent plugs on the system, pumping fuel through until it is free of bubbles. Then, while you're still pumping, you shut off the vents. It's like bleeding a hydraulic brake system on a car.

Instructions for the Perkins engine with in-line fuel injection pump are typical. On that diesel, you proceed as follows:

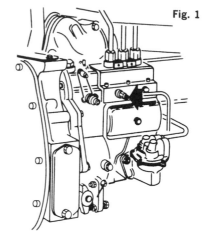

Fig. 1

Fig. 1 Arrow indicates location of injection pump bleed screw on a Perkins diesel. Design is typical.

1. Unscrew the final filter vent plug.

2. Unscrew the two vent plugs or vent screws on the fuel injection pump by two or three turns. These plugs are fitted each side of the fuel inlet connection.

3. Operate the priming lever on the fuel lift pump. When bubble-free fuel issues from the venting points, tighten the fuel filter vent plug and then the injection pump vent plugs.

Instructions for bleeding the Lehman-Ford diesel are similar:

1. Loosen the bleed screw on the inlet side of the fuel filter several turns.

2. Operate the priming lever on the side of the fuel pump until bubble-free fuel flows; then close the screw.

3. Loosen bleed screw on the outlet side of the filter and repeat the operation.

4. Two additional bleed screws are found on the injection pump assembly. First, loosen the screw nearest the inlet line; then pump fuel through until it runs clear of bubbles. Repeat the operation on the last bleed screw.

After you've bled air from the fuel system of your diesel, it's a good idea to operate the engine at dockside for five or ten minutes, making sure all air's purged, and the engine is happy.

Fig. 2

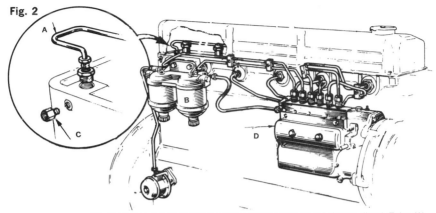

Fig. 2 Engine-mounted fuel handling components on a Lehman diesel. Tube (A) returns excess fuel to the tank; filters (B) are the secondary filters; connector (C) is for the return line; and the injection pump cover is part (D).

Fig. 3   Fig. 3 Procedure for venting Volvo engine is typical for most diesels.

1	Open venting screw on the fuel filter about 4 turns. Be observant for fuel leakage.
2	Pump up the fuel by using the hand primer until fuel, free from air bubbles flows out. Close venting screw. If the pump action is poor, turn the engine so that the cam driving the pump changes position.
3	If the injection pump has been removed, or when first starting a new engine, the injection pump must be vented. Open the venting screw on the injection pump about 2 turns. Pump the hand primer until fuel free from air bubbles flows out. Close the venting screw.
4	Loosen the injector's delivery pipe nut, push in the stop control and put the engine speed control in the full speed position. Press down the cold start button (MD11C only). Turn the engine by using the starter motor until fuel flows out from the delivery pipes. Retighten the delivery pipe nut and start the engine.

Keep the Air Cleaner Clean

Diesels are great air gulpers, needing lots of fresh, clean air. When you throttle back a gasoline auxiliary engine, you reduce the volume of air which it breathes per revolution. Not so with the diesel; it sucks in a full cylinder of air at each stroke, regardless of fuel setting. Most diesels are fitted with an air filter or cleaner to purify the induced air, protecting the engine's internals against abrasion. One of your boat-keeping chores is to keep this filter clean. It's important to do so, to keep the engine from being choked. Some filter elements are washable or cleanable, others are of the replaceable variety. Proceed accordingly.

Keep the Fuel Filters Clean

Air in diesel fuel will stop the engine. But dirt in the fuel will wreck it. It's far more important that diesel fuel be maintained free of water and dirt than that gasoline be kept pristine. The majority of diesels have at least a primary fuel filter and water separator followed by a secondary filter. Some engines are fitted with the primary, secondary and yet another secondary filter, assuring that only the purest liquid reaches the injectors. It's up to you to keep these filters serviced.

As a minimum, inspect the primary filter, the one nearest the fuel tank, once a week. Change the elements in the secondary filters once a season. However, should you ever take aboard a dose of dirty fuel, or if water gets through to the secondary filters (the ones near the injector pump assembly) change all elements and then bleed the system of air. On most diesels it's required that you do a bleed job whenever you change the secondary filters. Regardless, it's a good idea, because bleeding the system is not that much of an operation.

Lubrication is Important

If good lubrication means a lot to the gasoline marine engine, it is twice as important to the diesel because of the latter's high working pressures. You must change the oil and filter regularly, and should use the best grade oil, one specifically refined for diesel use. Most manufacturers recommend that both oil and filter be changed after the initial 15 hours of operation and each 200 hours after that. If you have any doubts about how long the oil has been in the crankcase,

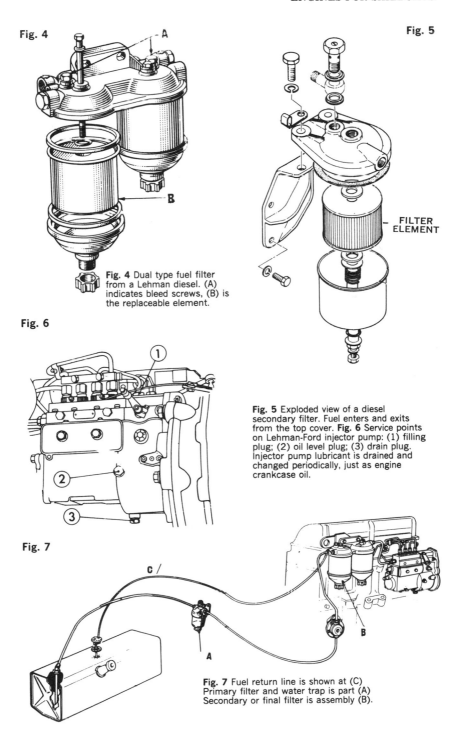

Fig. 4

A

B

Fig. 4 Dual type fuel filter from a Lehman diesel. (A) indicates bleed screws, (B) is the replaceable element.

Fig. 5

FILTER ELEMENT

Fig. 6

(1)

(2)

(3)

Fig. 5 Exploded view of a diesel secondary filter. Fuel enters and exits from the top cover. **Fig. 6** Service points on Lehman-Ford injector pump: (1) filling plug; (2) oil level plug; (3) drain plug. Injector pump lubricant is drained and changed periodically, just as engine crankcase oil.

Fig. 7

C

A

B

Fig. 7 Fuel return line is shown at (C) Primary filter and water trap is part (A) Secondary or final filter is assembly (B).

change it and the filter without a qualm. The engine will be glad you did.

Scheduled Maintenance

From one engine to another, details vary somewhat, but the general principles of routine diesel maintenance are the same. The summary given here, with minor modification, can be applied to diesels such as the Lehman-Ford, Perkins, Westerbeke, Yanmar, Volvo, and the like. You might like to modify this schedule to suit yourself and keep a copy of it in your log book or plaster it somewhere in the engine compartment as a reminder.

After First 15 hours

1. Change the engine oil.
2. Tighten cylinder head bolts.
3. Adjust valve clearance.
4. Examine zinc anti-corrosion pencil in heat exchanger.
5. Adjust V-belt tension.
6. Measure oil level in injection pump assembly.
7. Check transmission oil level.
8. Service the intake air filter.
9. Inspect the engine-to-prop-shaft alignment.
   (Do this twice a year.)
10. Adjust idling speed, if required.

Every 10 Hours of Running

11. Measure transmission and crankcase oil levels.
12. Inspect cooling water level on closed systems.

Every 50 Hours of Running

13. Service intake air filter.
14. Measure oil level in injection pump assembly.
15. Examine zinc anti-corrosion pencil in heat exchanger.

Every 200 Hours of Running

16. Adjust V-belt tension. Replace frayed belts.
17. Change oil in injection pump assembly.
18. Change engine and transmission oil.
19. Change lube oil and fuel oil filters, all.
20. Clean fuel lift pump.
21. Clean injection pump cover filter.

Every 400 Hours of Running or Every Two Years

22. Remove and service injectors. Note: Servicing should be done in qualified shop having the required equipment.

23. Adjust valve clearances.

24. Remove raw water pump and inspect drive coupling. Inspect the pump impeller, replacing it if it is worn or chewed.

25. Adjust the idling speed, if necessary.

Ten "Must" Rules for Everyday Operation

J. H. Westerbeke asks users of its marine diesels to observe ten *must* rules when operating the company's diesels. These rules are applicable to the operation of just about any diesel, since they are mostly common sense:

ALWAYS—

1. Keep the engine manual handy and read it whenever in doubt.

2. Use only *filtered* fuel, and check lube oil level daily.

3. Check cooling water temperature frequently, making sure it is 190°F or cooler.

4. Close all drain cocks and top up with water before starting out.

5. Investigate any oil leak immediately, no matter how small.

NEVER—

1. Race the engine in neutral.

2. Run the engine unless the gauge shows proper oil pressure.

3. Break the fuel pump seals.

4. Use cotton waste or fluffy cloth for cleaning.

5. Store fuel in a galvanized container.

6. Subject the engine to prolonged overload or continued running if black smoke belches from the exhaust.

The Daily Run, With and Without Trouble

Perkins engineers give the following practical hints on running their marine auxiliary diesels. The suggestions are general enough to apply to all diesels in a great majority of cases:

If the engine stops, the first thing to do is see that the fuel supply valve is on, and that there is fuel in the tank. If the engine ran until the fuel tank was completely empty, there is a good chance that dirt has been drawn into the fuel lines. Don't try to run again until you re-fuel, change the fuel filters, and bleed the system. Dirty fuel is the great diesel killer.

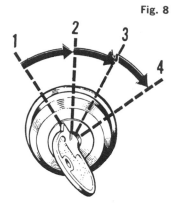

Fig. 8

Fig. 8 Some Volvo diesels use a special "ignition" key for starting: Position (1) is off; (2) is engaging position; (3) is to energize the glow plugs which are starting aids; (4) energizes the starter motor.

If the engine slows down or loses power, there could be something wrapped around the propeller. Always investigate this first. Inspect the air intake for obstruction, the air filter for excess dirt, and the engine compartment for a good supply of air. (Cases are known where the engine compartment was so tight and ill-ventilated that the engine lost power when the hatch cover was secured.)

If engine coolant boils, immediately ease off on the throttle and try to find the cause. Test the sea cock, making sure it's wide open and that mud or silt have not clogged the water pick-up. Maybe you were aground. If you've a trash trap or water strainer installed, see that it is unobstructed. Check raw water pump operation; perhaps the impeller has failed. Make sure water is flowing from the outlet, usually via the exhaust.

If a high-pressure fuel pipe (one serving an injector) springs a leak, disconnect it and direct the flow of fuel into a can or other receptacle. Continue running on the remaining cylinders. On *no* account attempt to flatten or pinch off the pipe; doing so will ruin the injector pump assembly. Leaks in low-pressure fuel pipes can be temporarily repaired with adhesive tape, hose, clamps and ingenuity.

Auxiliary installations may require the engine to run while the yacht is beating to windward. Under these conditions, the boat may heel up to 30° without adverse effect on the lubrication system, provided she is righted occasionally in order to lubricate the valve gear.

If a serious oil leak occurs, shut down the engine immediately; then try to find the cause. Oil leaks are hard to cure temporarily because of the pressure involved. However, if you can stem the main

DIESEL FAULT FINDING CHART

TROUBLE   POSSIBLE CAUSE

Slow cranking speed . . . . . 1, 2, 3, 4.

Will not start 5, 6, 7, 8, 9, 10, 12, 13, 14, 15, 16, 17, 18, 19, 20, 22, 31, 32, 33

Difficult starting . . . . 5, 7, 8, 9, 10, 11, 12, 13, 14, 15, 16, 18, 19, 20, 21, 22, 24, 29, 31, 32, 33.

Lack of Power . . . . 8, 9, 10, 11, 12, 13, 14, 18, 19, 20, 21, 22, 23, 24, 25, 26, 27, 31, 32, 33.

Misfiring . . . . 8, 9, 10, 12, 13, 14, 16, 18, 19, 20, 25, 26, 28, 29, 30, 32.

Excessive fuel consumption . 11, 13, 14, 16, 18, 19, 20, 22, 23, 24, 25, 27, 28, 29, 31, 32, 33.

Black exhaust smoke . . . . . 11, 13, 14, 16, 18, 19, 20, 22, 24, 25, 27, 28, 29, 31, 32, 33.

Blue white exhaust . . . . . . 4, 16, 18, 19, 20, 25, 27, 31, 33, 34, 35, 45, 56.

Low oil pressure . . . . 4, 36, 37, 38, 39, 40, 42, 43, 44, 58.

Knocking . . . . 9, 14, 16, 18, 19, 22, 26, 28, 29, 31, 33, 35, 36, 45, 46, 59.

Erratic running . . . . 7, 8, 9, 10, 11, 12, 13, 14, 16, 20, 21, 23, 26, 28, 29, 30, 33, 35, 45, 59.

Vibration . . . . 13, 14, 20, 23, 25, 26, 29, 30, 33, 45, 48, 49.

High oil pressure . . . . 4, 38, 41.

Overheating . . . . 11, 13, 14, 16, 18, 19, 24, 25, 45, 47, 50, 51, 52, 53, 54, 57.

Excessive crankcase pressure 25, 31, 33, 34, 45, 55.

Poor compression . . . . 11, 19, 25, 28, 31, 32, 33, 34, 46, 59.

Starts and stops . . . . 10, 11, 12.

KEY TO FAULT FINDING CHART

1. Battery capacity low
2. Bad electrical connection
3. Faulty starter motor
4. Incorrect grade of lube oil
5. Low cranking speed
6. Fuel tank empty
7. Faulty stop-control operation
8. Blocked fuel feed pipe
9. Faulty fuel
10. Choked fuel filter
11. Restriction in air cleaner
12. Air in fuel system
13. Faulty fuel injection pump
14. Faulty atomizers or incorrect pipe
15. Incorrect use of cold-start equipment
16. Faulty cold starting equipment
17. Broken fuel injection pump drive
18. Incorrect fuel pump timing
19. Incorrect valve timing
20. Poor compression
21. Blocked fuel tank vent
22. Incorrect type or grade of fuel
23. Sticking throttle or restricted movement
24. Exhaust pipe restriction
25. Cylinder head gasket leaking
26. Overheating
27. Cold running
28. Incorrect tappet adjustment
29. Sticking valves
30. Incorrect high pressure pipes
31. Worn cylinder bores
32. Pitted valves and seats
33. Broken, worn, or sticking piston ring (s)
34. Worn valve stems and guides
35. Incorrect grade of oil in air cleaner
36. Worn or damaged bearings
37. Insufficient oil in sump
38. Inaccurate gauge
39. Oil pump worn
40. Pressure relief valve sticking open
41. Pressure relief valve sticking closed
42. Broken relief valve spring
43. Faulty suction pipe
44. Choked oil filter
45. Piston seizure
46. Incorrect piston height
47. Strainer or weed trap blocked
48. Faulty engine mounting
49. Incorrectly aligned flywheel or housing
50. Faulty thermostat
51. Restriction in water jacket
52. Loose water pump drive belts
53. Gearbox or engine oil cooler choked
54. Faulty water pump
55. Choked breather pipe
56. Damaged valve stem oil deflectors
57. Coolant level too low
58. Blocked sump strainer
59. Broken valve spring

flow to a drip or dribble, place a can underneath the leak and replenish the engine with new oil at the same rate as the loss. (Good reason to carry a few quarts of crankcase oil aboard at all times.)

A drip tray of metal or fiberglass should be secured beneath the engine to stop lube oil or fuel from dripping into the bilge. Keep the tray clean, then you'll be able to see fresh drippings, should the engine spring even the slightest leak.

Trouble-Shooting (Here's Murphy's Law Again)

Elsewhere in the book we stated that the diesel was generally more reliable as auxiliary power than the gasoline engine. And that is true. Nevertheless, it's a machine, and can misbehave. When it does, you may want to consult this trouble-shooting chart. The chart is broken into two sections: the trouble section and the key to trouble finding. Prepared by engineers of Perkins Engines, the chart applies to just about any make of conventional diesel.

IX
Keeping the
Outboard Auxiliary
Happy

For boats up to about 25 feet, there's a lot to recommend the outboard auxiliary: It occupies little or no useful space on the boat; it is light of weight and small in size. Removable for maintenance, service, and winter storage, its parts are universally available, and mechanics the world over are familiar with its relatively simple innards.

Compared to installing an inboard, clamping on an outboard is a snap. And when you're under sail, its lower unit can be retracted, reducing its drag to zero. The motor requires no messy oil or filter changes, and while you're under way on a long offshore passage, the outboard can be stored almost anywhere on the boat. When you reach port, the outboard auxiliary can do double duty, providing muscle-saving power for your dink.

Notwithstanding its merits, the outboard isn't all roses: On an otherwise beautiful yacht, it appears as an incongruous blob on the transom (unless it's in a special well). The outboard smells; it can be offensive in a following wind. Exposed to the elements, it takes a beating in foul weather, and it's clumsy to handle in sizes larger than 20 hp. That limits the outboard to boats of modest tonnage. The outboard uses much more fuel than the diesel, and even is thirstier than the inboard 4-cycle gasoline engine. Yet another drawback is the outboard's inability to furnish the heavy direct currents required to charge big batteries, energize extensive electronic gear, and operate direct-current refrigerators. Conversely, the inboard, even the smallest one, can be fitted with an oversize alternator capable of delivering all the kilowatts desired by comfort-loving yachtsmen and yachtswomen.

Fig. 1 An attractive feature of outboard auxiliary power is that the little motor can do double duty, powering the dink when you reach port.

Appropriate outboards are available from a couple of horsepower for small daysailers to 15 or 20 hp. for weekenders and cruisers. The smallest models, those in the two-to four-hp. class, have integral fuel tanks; larger motors have remote tanks connected by plastic fuel hose. Remote tanks are a great convenience, eliminating the gymnastics associated with fueling a motor that hangs out from the transom.

When buying outboard auxiliary power, lean toward specifying thrust or "push" rather than simple brute horsepower. Most outboard companies offer special sailboat models with extended lower units, greater gear reduction, and larger propellers having less than standard pitch. These motors warrant your consideration: For a given weight and power, they will push your boat harder.

For planning, and to help you estimate the effect of the outboard's weight on the trim of your boat, use the weights in the following tabulation:

These weights are the approximate values for manually started

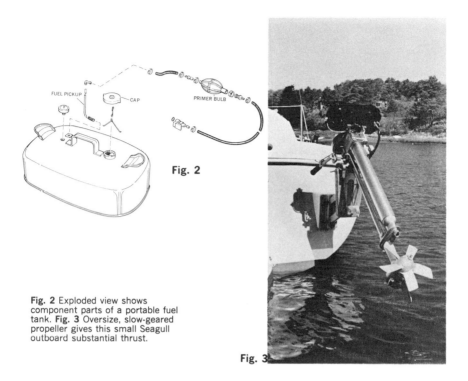

Fig. 2

Fig. 2 Exploded view shows component parts of a portable fuel tank. Fig. 3 Oversize, slow-geared propeller gives this small Seagull outboard substantial thrust.

Fig. 3

units. Electric start models, where available, weigh some ten pounds more. The battery for an electric start model adds another 35 pounds, but of course this added weight is not hung on the transom,

Horsepower	Pounds Weight
2	25
4	30
5	35
6	45
10	65
15	70
25	100

and may be carried almost anywhere convenient to the motor, subject to the length and run of cables.

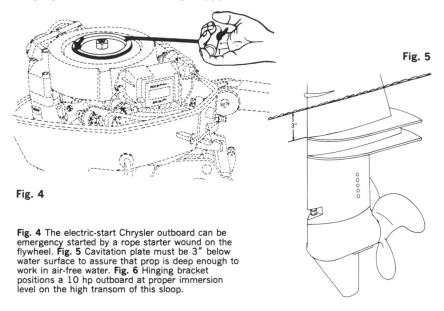

Fig. 5

Fig. 4

Fig. 4 The electric-start Chrysler outboard can be emergency started by a rope starter wound on the flywheel. **Fig. 5** Cavitation plate must be 3″ below water surface to assure that prop is deep enough to work in air-free water. **Fig. 6** Hinging bracket positions a 10 hp outboard at proper immersion level on the high transom of this sloop.

On first thought it would appear silly to select a motor capable of driving your boat faster than normal hull speed. Sometimes however, a little extra power is appreciated. For one thing, it allows you to cruise at part throttle; but more important still, it will push your yacht, including all its hamper aloft, into a fresh breeze. Sometimes, particularly off a lee shore, this can be comforting.

If the motor is mounted where it's difficult to reach, electric starting is an almost-vital accessory. Available on motors as small as six hp., starters offer the advantage that the rig can be started without your waltzing about on a slippery deck or hanging stern-high into a motor well. Another advantage is the convenience of electricity available from their battery-charging alternators. In a pinch, of course, the electric-start outboard can be rope started, and that's more than can be said for many inboard engines.

Long shafts or shaft extensions are available for many outboards. If your boat's transom is too high for a standard outboard, you'll want the long-shaft version. You'll be able to judge required length inasmuch as outboards are designed to operate efficiently with their

Fig. 6

cavitation plate two or three inches below the water. If the cavitation plate is at the surface or above, the outboard's propeller will be unable to get a grip on the water and will fail to develop full thrust.

If you intend to maneuver your boat under power in tight quarters, get a motor with forward, neutral and reverse operation. Most motors five hp. or bigger have this feature. With gearshift, you can execute much better maneuvers than with a motor which must be swiveled 180° in its mount to achieve reverse. While being turned through the 180° arc, such a motor momentarily pulls the boat to one side.

Mounting an outboard on a transom with reverse slope requires a special mounting block or bracket. The motor must be leveled so its lower unit is approximately vertical to the water as the boat proceeds underway. If the prop unit on any sailboat is angled too far out from the transom, the thrust of propulsion will tend to sink the stern and raise the bow. If the lower unit is angled inward, thrust will force the stern up, making the bow plough down into the water. A little experimenting with the boat underway will indicate best angle.

The motor can then be secured to this angle permanently, an adjustable bracket or tilt pin allowing angle to be easily set.

If possible, mount your motor on the transom's centerline, or, on a boat with outboard rudder, as close to the center as feasible. A motor mounted far to port tries to force the boat into a constant starboard turn, and vice versa. Off-center mounting also makes the yacht more difficult to manage in reverse.

However, if your boat's design forces you to mount the motor off-center, consider this: If it has a right-hand wheel, one rotating clockwise viewed from astern, mount the motor on the port side of the transom. Prop torque will then tend to cancel off-center steering effect.

Regardless of where you mount the outboard, provide it with a stout safety cord, chain, or lanyard. This will prevent it from sinking, should it slip its moorings from transom or well.

Fuel supplies for outboards are beautifully simple and, properly handled, are safe. The smallest rigs have integral tanks, requiring no connecting tubing. However, the majority of outboard auxiliaries have separate six-gallon tanks which can be positioned in any well-ventilated location reasonably close to the motor.

Virtually all modern outboard motors burn a mixture comprising 1 part lubricating oil to 50 parts of gasoline by volume. The following table shows the relationship of this 2% mixture in popular measures:

Gasoline Quantity	Oil Quantity
1 gallon	1/6 pint (2.6 ounces)
3.8 liters	0.08 liters
6 gallons	1 pint (16 ounces)
23 liters	0.5 liters

Outboard auxiliaries run on ordinary automobile gasoline, regular-leaded, or lead-free 85 octane as placarded on the gas pump. They don't like low-octane white gasoline, naptha, or white fuel intended for Coleman lanterns. Other than that, the outboard is not terribly fussy about its fuel.

By contrast, lubricating oil is a cat of another stripe. To keep your rig running well and to prevent its fouling the plugs and combustion

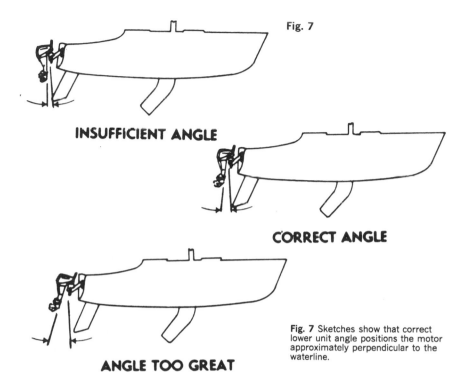

Fig. 7

INSUFFICIENT ANGLE

CORRECT ANGLE

ANGLE TOO GREAT

Fig. 7 Sketches show that correct lower unit angle positions the motor approximately perpendicular to the waterline.

chambers, use outboard motor oil marketed by the motor manufacturer, or that which is BIA certified for service TC-W (two-cycle water-cooled). Yes, Virginia, there really is a difference in oils; it's not just a sales gimmick to make you purchase the special product. Major oil companies manufacture lube with special qualities and burnability strictly for outboards, and it's worth using.

What if you can't locate outboard oil in some boondock? In an emergency, use ordinary automobile non-detergent SAE-40 oil, but increase the gasoline/oil ratio to 25:1, which is two pints in 6 gallons. Return to the high-proof stuff as soon as possible.

Just as building a decent martini requires a certain touch of care, so does mixing gasoline and oil in your outboard's tank. The basics of this operation are:

1. Never use stale fuel, i.e., gasoline that has aged in the tank for several weeks or more. This is worse for the engine than excess vermouth in a supposedly dry martini. Stale gasoline may induce gum or varnish inside the motor.

2. Maintain a scrupulously clean fuel tank. If at all possible, strain all fuel through a fine mesh strainer. There are tiny orifices in the outboard carburetor; the smallest bits of dirt will clog these.

3. Pour about a gallon of gasoline into the portable tank. Add the required oil. Cap the tank and slosh the mixture about as though you were preparing a whiskey sour. Then open the tank and add the balance of gasoline.

4. If your yacht has a built-in tank, follow this simple procedure when gassing up: In a portable container, mix all the required lube with a gallon or more of gasoline. Using a large filter funnel, pour this mixture into the funnel along with gasoline from the dockside pump. The liquid mixture reaching the tank will be reasonably homogeneous.

Starting procedures vary a little from one motor to another, but the principles remain the same, and the pitfalls leading to starting problems spring from the same mistakes. Keep the following in mind before firing up old Betsy:

1. Prior to yanking the cord or hitting the starter switch, make sure you've plenty of fuel mixture in the tank. Many a hard-start Donnybrook originated with an empty gas tank.

2. Connect the fuel line (unless the tank is integral) and prime the carburetor by squeezing the primer bulb until it feels hard. With integral tanks, open air vent in filler cap and fuel-line valve just below the tank.

3. Make sure the gearshift is in neutral. Most motors will not fire if in gear, but some older ones have no interlock and may start in gear, slamming your boat up against the pier or another yacht.

4. If the engine is cold, pull out the choke. Crack the throttle open to "START."

5. Pull the starter cord gently until you feel the engaging mechanism grip the flywheel; then yank smartly—but don't pull the rewind cord all the way to its stop. Repeat this three or four times as required to make her fire and run.

6. After the engine starts, push in the choke. If the carburetor pops and the motor threatens to stall, use partial choke until she's warm enough to run without choke.

Suppose you yank on the starter cord a half dozen times or more,

Fig. 8

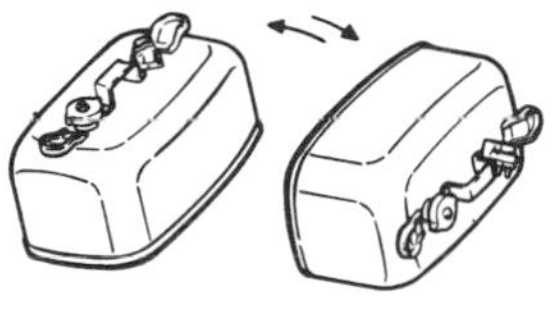

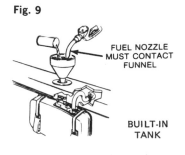

PORTABLE TANK

Fig. **8** After gasoline and oil are poured into the portable tank, the contents should be mixed by being sloshed about. Fig. **9** Gasoline and oil are poured together through a funnel to fill the built-in tank serving an outboard auxiliary. **Fig. 10** An in-line squeeze bulb draws fuel from the tank, feeding the outboard until its internal fuel pump can deliver fuel to the carburetor.

Fig. 9

Fig. 10

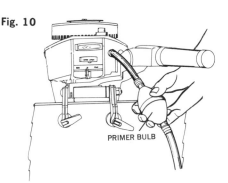

FUEL NOZZLE
MUST CONTACT
FUNNEL

BUILT-IN
TANK

PRIMER BULB

or you crank with the electric starter five to 10 seconds, but the beast refuses to snarl?

Sniff about and see if she's getting gas. If she is, the crankcase and cylinders are probably flooded. Proceed as follows:

Open the choke. Open the throttle wide. Crank the engine a couple of dozen revolutions. If you're using a hand-starter cord, crank quite slowly. Then close the throttle to the correct starting position, and try again for a start.

If it seems obvious that the motor is badly flooded, remove the spark plugs, ground the spark plug wires to the head, and crank the engine, preferably with open throttle and gas line disconnected. If the spark plugs are wet with gasoline, dry them or substitute a spare set before you try another start.

Breaking in your new outboard auxiliary requires no great application or science, but you might observe the following:

1. Use only BIA-certified TC-W oil in the ratio recommended for regular operation.

2. Start the engine and run at moderate speed, a little less than half-throttle under load, for perhaps 10 minutes. Make sure the water pump is operating and that water squirts from the outlet.

3. Run the boat about half-throttle; advance to full throttle for two

or three seconds. Then, immediately return to moderate speed for five minutes.

4. Repeat step 3, gradually increasing time of full throttle operation until five minutes of full bore have been reached. This break-in period should take about an hour and a half, and extended full bore operation should be avoided until after the motor has three hours of use.

If your metal outboard breeze is fitted with a gearshift, don't be too rough on the lever. Never shift at engine speeds much above idle or you may damage the shift mechanism. Don't force the lever; avoid trying to shift into gear while the engine is not running. When you shift, do so with a quick, deft, snapping action; never ease the engine into gear or you'll prematurely wear the splines on the dog clutches. Snappy engagement and disengagement is the proper style.

When you throw her into reverse, backing the boat, be extra-careful not to wallop submerged objects or run aground. In reverse, the lower unit can't kick up, as it can when going forward. If you plough into something, the lower unit will transmit all shock directly to the transom or motor well. Not only might the outboard be damaged, but the boat could be, as well. The moral: Take it easy in reverse.

"Man overboard!" That cry of alarm is cause for immediate action on any yacht. "Motor overboard!" is not nearly so serious a situation, but if the rig can be recovered, reasonably prompt action can save it for continued service.

The best thing you can do for the motor recovered after a dunking is to get it to a respectable motor repair shop, and let the mechanics dry it out and test it. This is especially important if the unit was submerged in salt water, a notorious enemy of ignition components. If the motor was running when it hit the water, professional attention is especially important because internal parts may have been damaged by water-hammer. An attempt to start this motor prior to disassembly may do more damage, converting a partial wreck to a total.

If your motor took her dunking whilst quiescent, try the following as quickly as possible after recovery:

1. Flush all parts with fresh, clean, warm tap water.

2. Remove the spark plugs. Crank the engine many times by hand to eject water from crankcase and cylinders. Manipulate the assembly into different positions as you do this.

3. If possible, use a portable paint sprayer compressor and blow into all crevices and the space under the flywheel. Blow into the spark plug holes while rotating the engine slowly.

4. Preferably, remove the flywheel and thoroughly dry all ignition parts. When they're bone-dry, spray the section with CRC or other moisture inhibitor.

5. Squirt plenty of outboard oil into the spark plug holes and rotate the engine to distribute this oil throughout the inside.

6. Bake the spark plugs bone-dry. Install them.

7. Drain fuel lines and carburetor. Blow out all traces of water.

8. If the fuel tank was submerged, drain it, flush it with gasoline and re-fill with the correct mixture of gasoline and lube.

9. Prime the engine in the usual way with the squeeze bulb; then give it a try. When it runs, give it a good workout, running under load for at least 30 minutes.

If you'll devote a couple of hours, may be less, each year to routine service and lubrication, it won't take any real time at all, because the effort will eliminate at least two breakdown hours. High points of owner service include these simple operations:

Service the spark plugs: Outboard spark plugs take a terrible beating and deserve routine attention. Most hard starting, missing, and lack of power boils down to defective plugs. To minimize plug troubles, remove each several times a year. Clean and inspect them, and if they don't look kosher, install a new set. Before inserting the plugs, measure their gaps and set them to specification. The usual spark plug gap is 0.030", but, if possible, look up the correct spec in your owner's manual before adjusting the plugs.

When you replace plugs, buy the right type. Gap them, and tighten them just-so, preferably using a torque wrench to the specified tightness, typically 18 pound-feet.

Clean the fuel filters: Many portable tanks have a filter screen on the bottom of the pick-up tube. Remove the tube and clean this screen once a season. If it looks gummy, clean it in solvent or acetone (nail polish remover). Also, if the screen appears to be contaminated with tar or gum, you'd better clean out the tank with solvent.

Clean the fuel filter located on the power head, usually on or close to the fuel pump. Good idea to have a fresh gasket handy when you reassemble the filter.

Inspect the prop: Look for nicks, dents, bent blades. Once a season, remove the propeller and lubricate the shaft. If the prop is driven by a shear pin, replace the pin, and put a couple of spares aboard for emergency use.

Note: Always disconnect the spark plug wires while fussing about with the prop. God forbid that the engine should fire while your hand is on the prop blades.

Tilt up the lower unit: When the motor is out of operation, tilt the lower unit out of the water to reduce corrosion and fouling. Disconnect the battery cables if the motor is an electric model.

Lubricate the assembly: Oil or grease fittings are found on most outboards. Give each a shot of lube twice a season; doing so will keep the brackets and control linkage operating freely. If the motor has an electric starter, smear a little light grease on the starter pinion gear. Spray a fine mist of oil on the entire exterior from time to time, and wipe it down.

Check the lubricant in the lower unit at mid-season, and definitely replace it at season's end. Take this tack:

1. With the motor upright in operating position, remove both upper and lower plug screws in the lower gearcase just ahead of the propeller. Allow the lube to dribble out, giving it plenty of time, certainly not less than 10 minutes.

2. Lower unit lubricant, typically EP90 outboard gear lube, comes in giant toothpaste tubes with filler nozzles. After the old lube has drained, insert the tube's nozzle into the *lower* plug screw hole and squeeze oil into the gearcase until it oozes out the upper hole. After about a half jigger of lube has flowed from the top hole, reinstall the top plug screw and tighten.

3. Remove the tube nozzle from the bottom hole and immediately install the lower plug.

4. *Again* remove the upper plug screw; then allow the motor to

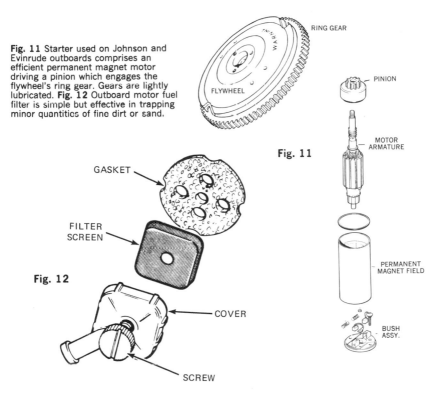

Fig. 11 Starter used on Johnson and Evinrude outboards comprises an efficient permanent magnet motor driving a pinion which engages the flywheel's ring gear. Gears are lightly lubricated. **Fig. 12** Outboard motor fuel filter is simple but effective in trapping minor quantities of fine dirt or sand.

stand upright for an hour. This will permit the viscous lube to completely fill all cavities in the gear housing. Recheck level, adding lube if necessary to bring level up to the top hole. Reinstall the top plug and tighten securely.

Note: When draining the lower unit, watch carefully for water. If the drippings are mixed with water, the lower unit needs attention, and the motor should be trundled off to your local friendly outboard shop for repairs.

Trouble-Shooting

The small outboard is a fairly simple machine. If kept dry, lubricated, and fueled, it should remain reasonably reliable. However, when Murphy's Law finally asserts itself, making the little monster misbehave, the following trouble-shooting chart should help you get it perking again:

OUTBOARD FAULT FINDING CHART

COMPLAINT   POSSIBLE CAUSE OF TROUBLE

Refuses to start . . . . 1, 2, 3, 5, 11, 13, 14, 16, 17, 18, 19, 20, 21, 22, 28, 29.
Starts but quits . . . . 1, 3, 4, 5, 6, 7, 8, 9, 10, 11, 12, 13, 15, 16, 17, 18, 19, 29.
Misses . . . . 4, 9, 10, 12, 13, 15, 16, 17, 18, 19, 21, 22, 28.
Idles badly or stalls . . . . 2, 4, 5, 6, 7, 8, 9, 10, 11, 12, 13, 15, 16, 17, 18, 19, 29.
Loses power . . . . 2, 4, 5, 6, 7, 8, 9, 10, 11, 12, 13, 15, 16, 17, 25.
Surges . . . . 13, 23, 25.
Vibrates or rumbles . . . . 23, 24, 25, 30.
Stops abruptly . . . . 3, 5, 6, 11, 22.
Overheats . . . . 12, 26, 27.
Knocks or pings . . . . 26, 27.
Backfires, spits through carb . . . . 4, 5, 6, 7, 8, 9, 11, 13, 15, 31.
Smokes excessively . . . . 12.
Fouls its plugs quickly . . . . 12, 15, 29.
Will not crank, either hand or electric . . . . . . 32.

POSSIBLE CAUSES OF TROUBLE

1. Remote fuel tank not tightly connected; integral tank fuel-line valve closed.
2. Remote controls, where used, need adjustment.
3. Empty fuel tank (don't laugh; it happens often!)
4. Fuel system dirty, clogged, or water-logged.
5. Fuel line kinked or pinched.
6. Fuel filters dirty or clogged.
7. Vent screw gasket obstructing air flow (vented tanks only).
8. Vent screw closed on tank filler cap (vented tanks only).
9. Air leak in induction system or crankcase.
10. Air leak in fuel system.
11. Carburetor passages dirty and clogged.
12. Incorrect fuel-oil mixture.
13. Carburetor out of adjustment.
14. Engine flooded.
15. Wrong type of spark plugs.
16. Defective or fouled spark plugs.
17. Ignition points out of adjustment, burned, or pitted.
18. Defective or wet ignition coils.
19. Defective ignition condenser.
20. Spark plug wires interchanged.
21. Frayed, cracked, wet or dirty spark plug wires.
22. Disconnected, grounded, or loose electrical wiring.
23. Propeller is cavitating.
24. Cavitation or loose flywheel.
25. Weed or rope snarled in propeller.
26. Blocked water intake.
27. Propeller too large or too much pitch.
28. Fuel-air mixture is too lean.
29. Fuel old and stale.
30. Loose mounting.
31. Engine is cold.
32. Water in cylinders.

Tools and Spares

A few tools and spare parts will help you keep your outboard ticking. Particularly if you plan to service the points, condenser, and coil, a flywheel puller is a necessity because on most small power heads the ignition components are under the wheel. Pack a sparkplug wrench and a few general hand tools. If the propeller is driven by a shear pin, carry several spares, and it's a good idea to include a spare prop in the kit. Several pints of outboard motor oil plus a general-purpose oil can will round out your duffle bag of outboard first aid material.

X
Sailboat Fuel Systems- Diesel and Gas

If the subject of sailboat fuel systems sounds a little boring, and you'd rather read about sails and rigging, let us try to seduce you into reading the chapter with a threat and a promise.

First the threat: If you don't know beans about what constitutes a decent sailboat fuel system your beloved may not be safe. In fact, she may be a fire trap.

Now the promise: If you'll work your way upwind through this chapter, your chances of sitting on a time bomb will be greatly reduced. What's more, your ability to trouble-shoot the system and get the engine going again will be enhanced threefold.

In the chapter on recommissioning, you'll find concrete hints on how to crawl around and inspect a fuel system. But in the present chapter we'll go a little deeper and describe the details which separate a safe, secure fuel supply rig from one which deserves naught but a boutonnière of scallions.

What's written here is not bilgewater conjured up in our heads. Our facts are based upon Coast Guard rules and proposed rules, plus safety standards derived by The American Boat and Yacht Council, an industry group that knows whereof it speaks.

Admittedly, you are not going to design a fuel system for your yacht; and we're not trying to convert you to marine engineering. But knowledge of what constitutes a decent fuel system will help you in evaluating the mechanical aspects of a new boat and will aid you in judging the worth of the system on your present vessel. The specifications here are purposely made tough enough for a gasoline installation, so that if your auxiliary is diesel, the specs are far more than adequate.

General Requirements of a Respectable System

While casting an eye on the fuel supply rig on your own boat, a friend's, or one you are considering buying, check off these requisites:

1. The entire system must be liquid-and vapor-tight to the boat's interior. Remember the *vapor tight* part of that dictum.

2. The system must be permanently installed with all components independently supported. That rules out long runs of copper tube which shake and flap like the luff of a sail.

3. All components shall be accessible. That means that you've got to be able to reach fuel valves, filters, and strainers without being a contortionist. Oh, skipper, how often is this rule violated by boat-builders!

4. It must be obvious to the beholder that the system as a whole is designed to withstand the rolling, heeling, pitching, and pounding which a sailboat can give it. This is just commonsense engineering.

Fuel Tanks

You don't have to be an expert mechanic to realize that if the fuel tank shifts, even slightly, it may fracture pipes or tubes connected to it. Therefore the first rule states that the tank must carry a plate stating its pedigree. Certified tanks have passed pressure, fire, vibration, and other strict tests required by ABYC and the Coast Guard. View with a jaundiced eye any tank that fails to have a nomenclature plate or label certifying its origins and stating the specifications to which it was tested.

The tank on any boat built in the past few years should carry a name plate with the following information:

Manufacturer's name

Year of manufacture

Capacity in gallons

Material specification and thickness

Fuel for which the tank is suitable

Maximum test pressure

"G" impact level to which the tank was tested

Experts take a dim view of a fuel tank made of terneplate (sheet iron or steel coated with solder). They don't like tanks of black iron or carbon steel. And they don't approve of any steel or iron tank which is encased in cellular plastic or fiberglass. Trapped moisture

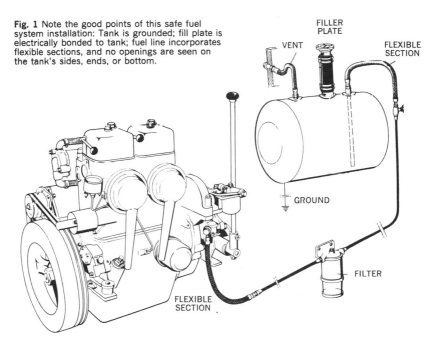

Fig. 1 Note the good points of this safe fuel system installation: Tank is grounded; fill plate is electrically bonded to tank; fuel line incorporates flexible sections, and no openings are seen on the tank's sides, ends, or bottom.

will cause corrosion of such tanks, and this will ultimately lead to leaks, often where they cannot be seen.

Non-rusting, non-corroding tanks of stainless steel or Monel metal are the best. They're expensive, but good. Aluminum tanks are also acceptable, but with a proviso: If aluminum is used it must be separated from copper or brass components by means of galvanic barrier. This means that copper fuel tubing may not be directly connected to an aluminum tank. There must be some kind of electrical insulation between tubing and tank. The purpose is to prevent leaks spawned by corrosion.

The fuel tank must have no openings, fittings, removable plates, plugs, drains, or valves on its bottom, sides, or ends. This safety rule is violated again and again, even on boats of good design and manufacture. How often you will see the fuel line entering the bottom of the tank! Or you'll see a clean-out "manhole" cover on the tank's side. Sometimes you'll see the most dangerous item of all: a draincock allowing fuel to be drawn off near the bottom of the tank. If anyone asks your opinion of this design shenanigans, tell them that it stinks, that it's unsafe, that the Coast Guard says so, and that you don't want to sail on a boat having such a timebomb in its bowels.

The tank must be designed so that water cannot puddle on top. And the tank must be installed where it cannot be reached by normal accumulations of bilge water.

Gasoline tanks must not be integral with the hull; they must be separate entities. However, diesel fuel tanks may be integral with the hull.

The tank should be accessible for inspection unless it is an aluminum tank which is foamed-in-place. (How many boats do you know where you are lucky to be able to *locate* the bloomin' tank, no less be able to inspect it!)

Aluminum tanks and non-metallic tanks may be foamed in place. This is allowed in compartments separated from other bilge spaces. The foam used to fill spaces around the tank must not be structural or a part of the boat's flotation requirement. While foamed-in-place tanks are technically acceptable, it is our private feelings that we'd rather see the tank out in the open where it can be inspected and watched. Apparently the experts agree.

Fuel Pipes, Tubing, and Accessories

The fill pipe running from deck to tank should have a minimum hose inside diameter of 1½ inch. The hose connections should be double clamped with good stainless steel clamps at least a half inch wide. Spring clamps are no good. They're not even fit for use on automobiles!

Here's a safety requirement that we see violated every day: The fuel fill opening must be located so that overflowing liquid cannot escape to the inside of the hull. Furthermore, it must be located so that vapors escaping from it do not flow into the boat. Where you see a boat with the fuel fill smack in the middle of the cockpit floor, you see a flagrant violation of this safety rule.

The deck plate should be marked with a fuel identification saying, "Diesel Fuel," or "Gasoline." We like to have the plate painted or circled in red. Water fill plates are blue or green, helping prevent a load of fuel from being pumped into our water supply, or vice versa.

The fill pipe must run as directly as possible, preferably in a straight line, from deck plate to tank. There must be no kinks or sharp bends in the fill arrangement.

Where rigid fuel lines terminate at an engine connection, a section of flexible line must be provided, and it must have enough slack to absorb engine vibration and motion due to torque. A flexible section should also be found at the fuel tank end of the line if there is any possibility of tank motion.

Fuel lines should be neatly run and well supported with clips or straps each 14 inches or closer. In the best installations, the fuel line is run above the level of the tank to a point close to the engine connection.

Vents

The sailboat fuel tank must be vented separately from its fill. Minimum hose inside diameter is 9/16″; and the vent pipe outlet must have a removable flame screen. Naturally, the vent must spill overboard, and should be arranged so that no matter how steeply the boat heels, water will not get back to the tank. The vent line should enter the tank at the latter's highest point, and it must not be connected in any way to the fill connection.

Filters

Each fuel system should have one or more filters because nothing kills an engine quicker than dirt reaching the diesel injection equipment or carburetor. The filter, to be of any use, must be readily available for cleaning and servicing. It shouldn't have any glass parts.

Fuel Shut-Offs

There should be a manual or electric fuel shut-off valve located in the line close to the tank. There should be another service valve in the line close to the engine. Proper valving is a simple requirement, but one often neglected.

Anti-siphon Protection

When the engine is stopped, or when a component leaks, perhaps when you're not aboard, you don't want fuel to siphon out of the tank and flood the bilge. The experts suggest several means of protecting against unwanted siphoning of fuel, and you can look for one of these on a good, safe system.

1. One method is to keep all fuel lines above tank level when the boat is in normal, unloaded, static flotation position. This is difficult on sailboats because it means the tank must be located low in the bilge, but it's obvious that if the fuel lines run uphill all the way,

siphoning is no problem.

2. A special anti-siphon valve is available and will solve the problems when properly mounted close to the fuel tank.

3. An electrically operated valve, close to the tank and open only when the diesel is running or the gasoline ignition switch is closed: such a valve will solve the problem.

4. A manually operated valve close to the tank will do the trick. Problem is, the skipper must remember to shut off the valve when he leaves the yacht.

Fuel Pumps

The fuel pump, particularly that on a gasoline auxiliary, should be designed from the ground up for marine service. It should not be the kind used on automobiles: These have an external vent allowing fuel to leak out of the assembly if the diaphragm is ruptured.

If your rig has an electric fuel pump, it should be wired so that it can run only if the engine is turning over. A momentary override switch for engine starting is OK. An electric fuel pump should be at the engine end of the fuel line, not at the tank end. This is a safety measure, even though some electric pump manufacturers state that their pumps "push" better than "pull."

Carburetors

A sidedraft or updraft carburetor, unless properly protected, can dribble gasoline into the bilge during a malfunction. An engine with this kind of carburetor must have a device which collects and holds fuel flowing out of the carb to the air intake. This gizmo must return the collected fuel to the engine intake system after the engine is re-started.

Grounding

Static electricity and electric sparks generated by unequal voltages in the fuel system can start fires. Therefore, every part of the system must be electrically tied together and the entire affair grounded. Experts say that resistance between the ground and each metal component of the fuel fill system should be 100 ohms or less. But from a practical standpoint, suffice it to say that the sailor should determine that the fill plate is electrically tied to the tank, the tank to the vent plate and so on.

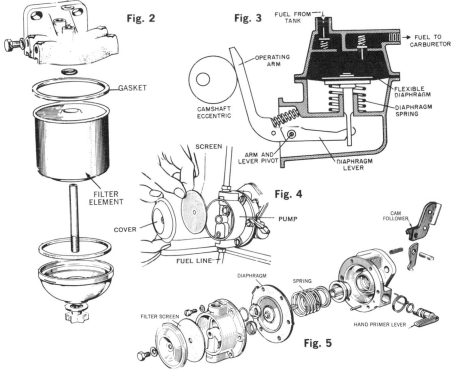

Fig. 2 Exploded view of a diesel fuel filter with replaceable element. Fig. 3 The housecat fuel pump is a diaphragm "gulper" type, actuated by the eccentric on the camshaft. Miniature spring-loaded valves are seen at the top. Diaphragm spring determines fuel pressure. Fig. 4 Changing the filter screen in a fuel pump. Fig. 5 Internal parts of a fuel transfer pump are seen in this exploded view. The cam follower is oscillated by an eccentric on the engine camshaft. Reciprocating motion is transmitted to the diaphragm via linkage, and fuel pressure is determined by the spring.

Chasing Fuel System Troubles

Above all, be careful, particularly when messing about with a gasoline system. The minute you start to tinker, demand that all smoking cease, that all fires and open flames on the boat be extinguished. Don't start the engine until the bilge is well aired.

A blocked fuel line is a common cause of engine stoppage. If the diesel injector assembly or gasoline engine's carburetor seems to be starved, first, make sure there's fuel in the tank sufficient to be picked up by the dip tube inside the tank. Next, be sure all valves are open. Then, carefully disconnect the fuel line at the pump and blow back through the line. If all valves are open, and there's no check valve, you should be able to blow air back to the tank, hearing it gurgle. This will usually clear a stoppage. (Refer to Chapter VIII for details on bleeding the diesel fuel system.)

Inspect the fuel strainers and filters. If they are dirty, clean them. A dirty filter will block fuel flow.

Flooding of the gasoline engine is just the opposite of a fuel blockage. If the engine refuses to start, but it smells of gasoline, and you're pretty sure it is flooded, proceed as follows to clear it:

1. Keep a fire extinguisher handy; then remove the flame arrester from the carburetor's air intake horn.

2. If the choke is manual, assure that it's wide open (not obstructing the flow of air). If it's automatic, hold it wide open with your finger.

3. Open the throttle *wide;* don't pump it.

4. With ignition on, crank the engine with the starter. It should start after a dozen revolutions or so. Reduce throttle setting to a snappy idle. And don't forget to replace the flame arrester; it's an important safety device, preventing flame from spitting out the carburetor intake and igniting vapors which might have accumulated in the bilge.

Diesels don't flood the same as gasoline engines. But in the rare instance that they get too much fuel in their cylinders, they run away wildly. Diesel runaway can occur if the governor breaks, if a governor linkage falls off, or if fuel oil is inadvertently poured into the air intake. If your diesel should ever go berserk (it's unlikely), stuff something into the air intake and choke it. That's the best way to stop the machine. Strangle it as quickly as possible; otherwise, if the runaway continues, the engine may destroy itself.

Occasionally, when it's hotter than Hades below decks, and when the engine itself is hot, vapor lock will block passage of gasoline to the carburetor. Vapor lock is the formation of gasoline vapor inside the fuel lines and pump. It's like gas on the stomach. The bubbles block the line, preventing fuel from getting through.

Vapor lock is most often encountered on a hot day after the engine has been stopped and an attempt is made to re-start it. Sometimes it starts, but then quits. The antidote is to cool the gasoline lines and fuel pump with cold wet rags. After the vapor inside the lines is condensed, the engine should function properly.

Tar, gum, and varnish can form in a fuel system of either the gasoline or diesel variety. If you leave fuel in the system for long periods, such as during lay-up, the liquid may deteriorate and create deposits of guk in the tank and lines. Two schools of thought oppose each other on what to do about fuel in the tank during lay-up: (See Chapter XVI)

1. The first theory states that the tank should be left completely full. This reduces the tank's breathing due to climatic changes. In doing so, it reduces condensation inside the tank, keeping water, gum formation, and corrosion to a minimum.

2. The second school of thought says, "Empty the tank completely." Granted, it will breathe and moisture will condense inside. But before it is refilled, it can be cleaned and filled with fresh fuel for the new season.

On his own boat, this writer takes the second tack, flushing the tank with a little acetone or lacquer thinner before filling it with fuel. It has the two advantages that the fuel is fresh and clean, and also the stored boat is lighter by the weight of fuel.

Should you find traces of gum or tar in your tanks or fuel lines, flushing through with acetone or lacquer thinner will remove it. Be careful. These solvents are as flammable as gasoline, and they're bad for your insides if you breathe their concentrated vapors.

Operating Safely

The best designed and maintained fuel system can be unsafe if the boat's skipper makes it so through careless operation. Even though you're an experienced sailor, you might want to brush up on your operating and fuel handling procedures by perusing the following. What's written here is aimed primarily at the sailor having a gasoline auxiliary. However, the man with a diesel does well to follow the same safe procedures.

Before fueling, shut down the engine; turn off all stoves and open flames; forbid smoking; close the cabin doors and ports.

While fueling, hold the pump's metal nozzle in contact with the metal deck fill plate.

After fueling and closing the fill, wipe up spilled fuel, or wash it down. Operate the bilge blower; open up the cabin and engine compartment.

Do *not* hit the starter switch until you have personally sniffed in the engine compartment. If you smell gas, hold everything; be sure the bilge is clean of fuel vapor before taking the plunge. This precaution applies anytime you are starting the engine, whether it's immediately after fueling or just a routine start at the beginning of the weekend.

XI

The Sailboat's Battery

The storage battery is certainly the heart of your auxiliary's electrical system. If it or its heavy wiring fails, you can't start your engine, gasoline or diesel, unless it's provided with a hand crank. Alternatively, if the engine is running, failure of the battery circuit will kill it, unless it's a gas engine with magneto ignition or a diesel.

Your sailboat's battery leads a harder life, in many ways, than the battery in your car. Often carrying heavy accessory loads, it sometimes sits a week or more at a time without being charged. In addition, after furnishing power for an engine start, it usually feels the influx of charging current for but a short interval, then it's thrown back to its own devices for another extended period after the boat's sails are set. To top off its woes, the battery lives in a damp, sometimes hot environment which accelerates its self-discharge rate.

Choosing a Battery

A battery's electrical capacity or size is usually expressed as its *ampere-hour rating*. A nominal 12-volt battery rated 60 ampere hours can deliver (theoretically) 60 amperes to its load for one hour, or 20 amperes for 3 hours. But these figures *are* theoretical and you must not count on getting the full number of advertised ampere-hours from a battery. If you should do any calculating, use half the rated ampere-hours and you will be living realistically.

A 12-volt battery rated 60 ampere-hours is a reasonable size for the gasoline auxiliary's starting battery. Diesels require larger batteries, the size varying widely with the type of engine. The diesel's battery should be rated for diesel service; ordinary automobile type batteries fall on their faces trying to do the job. Diesel batteries have heavier plates, fatter internal connectors, and more rugged terminations. Such construction is required because, while the battery is cranking the diesel, it must furnish terrific momentary current. This is more whap than the conventional gasoline engine starting battery can handle in the pinches, such as when engine and battery are cold.

When buying a boat battery, order the type with longer guarantee, such as 36 months. Buy a good brand, preferably one specifically rated for marine service. Surrette is the trade name of one such battery. From the outside, batteries look pretty much alike. But the better ones have improved internal construction, tougher plates, and design that prevents internal short circuits, particularly when the battery is constantly rolled and pounded—which it surely is aboard your sailboat.

Multiplying Reliability

The most intelligent thing you can do to assure that your auxiliary's starting battery will always have the power to kick the engine over is this: Provide one battery exclusively for engine starting; then install another or a series of others to handle accessories such as lights, pumps, blowers, and possibly a refrigerator. However, beware that refrigerator, about which we will have more to say subsequently.

The engine-starting battery, independent of all other loads, should have its own alternator or generator. With such an arrangement, the auxiliary's "private" battery should always be in good shape regardless of how badly the other battery bank is discharged.

For the ultimate in engine starting reliability on the cruising sailboat, the batteries which serve accessories should have their own alternator. The boat should also be equipped with a set of jumper cables so that in an emergency, the accessory batteries can be used to start the auxiliary engine. Alternately, a selector switch can be wired into the circuits, allowing the accessory batteries to be switched over for starting. The disadvantage to this, however, is that the starting battery may be inadvertently connected to the accessory batteries while they are in use. The starting battery might then be discharged along with its brother.

Battery Installation

A decently installed battery does not merely sit on a platform, it

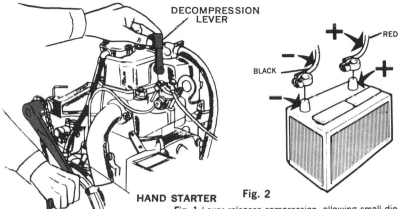

HAND STARTER **Fig. 2**

Fig. 1 Lever releases compression, allowing small diesel to be hand cranked with reasonable ease when its battery dies. **Fig. 2** Positive cable to positive battery post; negative to negative is a firm rule. Remember: red is positive; black is negative on most cables.

is enclosed in a proper box, secured against any kind of movement. Nor should the battery be buried under a lot of machinery; it's got to be readily accessible for inspection and service. When you're shopping for a new boat, that's something to watch for.

Cables must be short and fat, clean and neat. The engine-starting battery should be as close to the engine as possible with cables dressed so that their routing is directly from battery to starter. Long, thin cables create voltage drop and degrade starter performance.

As we point out in the chapter on recommissioning, battery posts and cable clamps must be kept clean. A little corrosion or dirt between the cable clamp and battery terminal can falsely signal dead battery. The cells will be fully charged, but the starter won't operate because corrosion acts as an insulator.

Disconnect Arrangement

The simplest arrangement for disconnecting the battery when you're away from the boat is to unclamp the cable. The technique is effective in preventing inadvertent discharge or fire, but it's a nuisance, and you are likely to neglect it when in a hurry. It's much better to have a good, approved type of battery disconnect switch, located close to the battery, and wired in the positive conductor. That's the hot or ungrounded conductor. The negative circuit represented by the ground strap connected to the engine block must never be opened unless the positive conductor is also open. Interrupting the ground circuit while the positive one is connected invites hardware corrosion due to stray currents.

When installing a disconnect switch in the battery circuit, select one that has an auxiliary switch for opening the voltage control circuit serving the alternator. This type is readily available in marine supply stores.

The reason for opening the alternator voltage control circuit when the battery charging circuit is disconnected is this: The alternator must never be operated into an open circuit while excited by a voltage regulator, which is telling it, in effect, to generate lots of electricity. If this should happen, the alternator may be destroyed. It is possible that someone may inadvertently open the master battery switch while the auxiliary engine is running. Unless the voltage control circuit is simultaneously opened, zap! there goes the alternator.

Where several batteries are available for starting the engine, you can install a switch marked "No. 1, "No. 2," "OFF," "BOTH." Switches of this kind are readily available, and with one properly wired, you can elect to start the engine with one battery, the other battery, or both together. Obviously, you can also disconnect both batteries; then, if one is defective, it will not drag down the other during the idle period. Such a switch is highly recommended by the experts.

Protection Against Rapid Discharge

We don't like the idea of using engine-starting batteries for operating heavy current accessories such as d.c. refrigerators. But where such items are operated by battery, even if not the starting battery, it is a splendid idea to make the following arrangement: Have a relay wired into the charging circuit which prevents operation of the high-draw accessory unless the engine is running and the alternator is charging. The accompanying drawing shows one way in which this can be done. With such an arrangement, the refrigerator (or whatever) cannot draw its high demand current unless that current (or most of it) is being returned to the battery by the engine's alternator or generator.

What is the Correct Charging Voltage?

Charging voltage is determined by the voltage regulator working

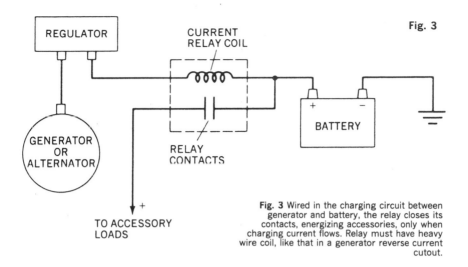

Fig. 3

Fig. 3 Wired in the charging circuit between generator and battery, the relay closes its contacts, energizing accessories, only when charging current flows. Relay must have heavy wire coil, like that in a generator reverse current cutout.

in conjunction with the engine-driven alternator or generator. Voltage determines the rate at which the battery will be charged and also the degree to which it will be charged. Excessive voltage may heat the battery, make it use too much water, and may damage its plates. Low voltage will take too long in charging the cells and, in sailboat service, may prevent the battery from ever getting fully charged.

In automobile, truck, and bus service, voltage regulators are ordinarily adjusted to about 14.5 volts. However, because of the low use factor associated with sailboat auxiliary engines and their alternators, it's perfectly acceptable to adjust the voltage regulator to 15 volts or even a hair more. This is the voltage delivered by the alternator to the battery when the cells are completely charged and there is no appreciable load on the system. It is best measured by a meter indicating from about 10 to 17 volts, designed specifically for the purpose. Volt-I-Cator and Chargicator are typical instruments for measuring battery charging voltages.

Using a Hydrometer

The hydrometer is a syringe having a glass test-tube section inside which is a float like a spar buoy. In testing a battery, you draw some of the electrolyte out of the cells, observing how high the calibrated float rises in the liquid inside the test tube. The bobber is calibrated in specific gravity, sometimes supplemented by red, yellow, and green segments indicating relative state of charge: low, fair, and full. Discharged specific gravity: 1.135; half charge: 1.197; and full charge: 1.260

Hydrometer response provides a reliable indication of a battery's state of charge, better than voltage, which can remain very close to nominal, even though the cells are nearly exhausted in a lightly-loaded battery. You should have a hydrometer in your kit of engine tools; it's a useful maintenance instrument.

Keep two points in mind when reading the hydrometer: It will indicate too low when the electrolyte is very warm, too high when the liquid is cold. Try to check the cells when battery temperature is between 75°F. and 80°F. The other caution is not to be alarmed by a low reading taken immediately after water has been added to the cells. After adding water, use the battery for a half hour before testing with your hydrometer.

What About Fast Charging?

Fast charging, charging a battery with 25 to 75 amperes, has a bad reputation. "That kind of charge will wreck my battery!" one boatman was heard to say. And, indeed, unless done properly, fast charging *can* destroy the cells.

However, fast charging, properly applied, is perfectly compatible with good practice, and you need not fear it *per se. Control* is the key to safe charging; the rate must be controlled so the battery does not overheat. Battery experts say that the cells may be charged at any rate that does not generate excessive gas or raise electrolyte temperature above +125°F for a short time. Another rule states that the fast rate is safe as long as it does not raise the voltage of any cell above 2.5 volts. That would indicate 15 volts for a nominal 12-volt battery.

Play it Safe

Whether being charged fast or slow, the cells emit gases. One of these is hydrogen, terribly explosive. Batteries should be in a well-ventilated compartment, admittedly a difficult arrangement aboard a sailboat. When a battery is under charge, give it extra ventilation, while keeping fires and sparks away. The author writes with particular authority on this subject because he once violated the rule: After

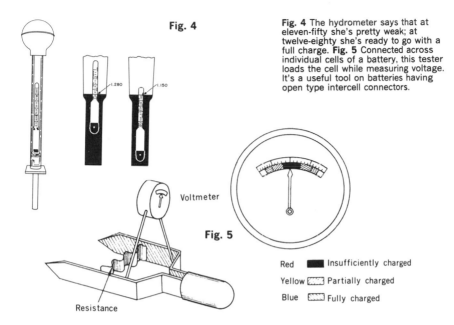

Fig. 4

Fig. 4 The hydrometer says that at eleven-fifty she's pretty weak; at twelve-eighty she's ready to go with a full charge. **Fig. 5** Connected across individual cells of a battery, this tester loads the cell while measuring voltage. It's a useful tool on batteries having open type intercell connectors.

Voltmeter

Fig. 5

Resistance

Red ▮ Insufficiently charged

Yellow ▨ Partially charged

Blue ▢ Fully charged

charging a battery quite briskly for an hour, he foolishly touched a live circuit wire to one of its terminal posts. Pow! The ensuing spark touched off an explosion that singed his hair, blew open a hatch cover, and cost him several years growth. Never will he pull that boob stunt again.

The moral is: provide adequate ventilation for the battery and keep sources of ignition away from it while it's charging.

Don't Overcharge

Discharging a battery to exhaustion and leaving it discharged for any length of time harms the cells. We've mentioned that before. Overcharge is hard on the battery, also. Too much charging can hurt the plates while reducing the battery's efficiency. Overcharging also creates excessive gassing, putting hydrogen into the compartment while shortening cell life. If a battery appears in good shape, but demands a lot of make-up water, it is being overcharged. To reduce charge rate from the alternator, slightly reduce system voltage. This is done by an adjustment on the voltage regulator. Unless you use your auxiliary very seldom, excess potential above 15-volts is likely to create the overcharged condition indicated by excessive water boil-off.

Constant Trickle Charging

In the chapter on recommissioning, we mention that it is not desirable to leave the battery on a constant-trickle charge all winter. The admonishment applies at all times. Charge your batteries at a decent rate, then turn off the charger. Don't trickle constantly at dockside.

Distilled or Tap Water?

"You should never use any but distilled or demineralized water in a storage battery," say some purists. Well, such pure water certainly is great. But battery manufacturers say that it's perfectly OK to use clean tap water provided it isn't famous for it's therapeutic mineral qualities. If you're in doubt about your local water, put a gallon jug of distilled H_2O aboard for the season. In any event, don't worry about the matter too much.

Troubles (Murphy's Law Again)

Numerous troubles can attack the battery and its allied circuits, but they're usually not hard to isolate. Popular troubles are these:

Battery loses charge rapidly: An internal fault or short circuit inside one of the cells will drain a battery in short order. A battery with this trouble will seemingly take a charge, but after an hour or perhaps even less, it will be all but dead. This will be true even though it is disconnected from all loads. The solution is to scrap the battery and buy a new one.

Electrical leaks in the boat's direct current system will drain the battery. The worse the leak, the faster will the battery be drained. If you leave the battery connected to its circuits during the week while you are away earning a living, and if it is dead each Friday evening upon your return, it may be that external circuit leakage is killing it. You can test for leaks as follows without expensive equipment: Make a simple test light as shown here, using two pieces of wire, a light socket, and a small-size, 12-volt dashboard light bulb.

Disconnect the positive battery cable from its terminal post. Open all the switches in the boat. Connect the test light in series between the battery post and cable clamp. The bulb must not glow, not even the tiniest bit viewed in the dark. If it does light up, ever so little, one of the boat's electrical circuits is leaky and is draining your

Fig. 6

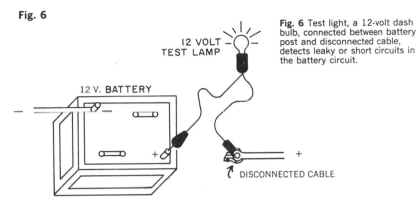

12 VOLT –(◯)– TEST LAMP

12 V. BATTERY

Fig. 6 Test light, a 12-volt dash bulb, connected between battery post and disconnected cable, detects leaky or short circuits in the battery circuit.

DISCONNECTED CABLE

battery.

What to do about the electrical leak?

The easy way out is to install a master battery switch which you will open whenever you are off the boat. (You should have this switch regardless.) But you don't want an electrical leak aboard, even where there's a master switch, so try to isolate the offending circuit.

Pull all the boat's 12-volt fuses from their holders, or open all the circuit breakers if these are used in place of fuses. Connect your test light between cable clamp and battery post. With all the circuits open, it should remain dark. Now, one at a time, replace the fuses, watching the test light as each fuse is back in its clip. When you replace the fuse in the leaky circuit, the test light will start to glow.

Once the defective circuit is identified, it's a matter of tracing through to find the specific trouble. The conductive fault may be via water-logged wires, through a defective switch, or across a wet insulator. Circuits associated with bilge, water pressure, or shower pumps are notorious offenders. These, I suggest, are best energized by a battery separate from that used for auxiliary engine cranking.

Battery Uses Excess Water: The charge rate is too high, and possibly the battery compartment is too hot. Reduce charging potential about half a volt. Check on ventilation. Shield the battery against direct radiation from hot engine manifolds or exhaust pipes.

Batteries Don't Last: You seem to be replacing batteries more frequently than owners of similar boats? Perhaps you are buying batteries of lower quality. Possibly you are making heavier demands on the d.c. system, accompanied by severe frequent discharge. Then too, shock and vibration may be severe, the battery being improperly installed. Check on that. Perhaps you are using make-up water extremely high in mineral content. Switch to demineralized or distilled water.

XII

Alternators and Generators

Both the newer alternator and older type conventional generator are used on auxiliary engines to charge the boat's batteries. Virtually all newer engines are fitted with automotive-type alternators, but there remain in use numerous auxiliaries with the older generator. Therefore, we'll not neglect that venerable machine.

The conventional generator closely resembles a shunt-wound direct current electric motor. In fact, if energized with d.c., it will run as a motor; (the alternator will not). On the outside of the generator you'll see two terminals: The first, usually of heavier hardware, is the generator's positive terminal, sometimes marked BAT because it is connected to the battery's positive post. The second generator terminal is the field connection. The magnitude of current flowing through this is varied by the voltage regulator, and determines the generator's charge rate.

Driven by a V-belt, the same as the conventional generator, the newer alternator is larger in diameter and shorter. Its drive pulley is often smaller than that on the generator, allowing it to spin the alternator faster for a given engine speed.

The alternator may have anywhere from one to four electrical terminations depending upon its design. But alternators are not as different in construction as this would indicate. The newest ones have their voltage regulators built-in, and these have but two terminals, one connected to the battery, the other to the ignition or diesel fuel cut-off switch.

Typical wire terminals on an alternator served by an external regulator are as follows, and would apply, for example, to the Leece-Neville model used extensively on auxiliaries.

"B+" terminal is the heavy stud which carries full alternator output to the battery. This termination is hefty because it will carry from 40 to 60 amperes.

"F" the field connection carries only a few amps of regulated exciter current from the battery via regulator to the rotating field.

The "B+" and "F" terminations are the principal ones, and some alternators have only these. But two more are optional:

"Neut" is a tap on the stator windings. (For the technically minded, the alternator is three-phase, star connected, with an ungrounded neutral.) The Neut connection delivers about 8 volts, this potential appearing only when the alternator is operating. The connection is usually used to operate a pilot light or relay which performs a secondary function not directly involved with charging the battery.

"Gnd" is a ground connection made to the frame of the unit. It simply provides a convenient point from which to ground the frame to the negative circuit, usually the engine block. On both the alternator and conventional generator, the unit's negative termination is its metal frame. Therefore, because the frame carries heavy currents, it must be well-connected to the engine block or head. Hard-to-locate charging problems sometimes originate with an alternator or generator which has loose mounting hardware.

Advantages of the alternator over the older generator are these: For its size, it delivers more charging current, and can do so when the engine idles. Generally, it is more reliable, uses a simpler regulator, and requires less maintenance. Disadvantages of the alternator are that it cannot charge an absolutely dead battery, and is instantly destroyed if the battery is ever installed backward in the boat.

That brings up the subject of reverse polarity:

Aboard an alternator-equipped sailboat, the battery must always be installed with its positive polarity (+) terminal connected to the positive (red) cable. The negative ground (−) cable or strap must be connected to the negative polarity battery post. If polarity is reversed, even for a second, pow! The alternator will be burned.

Inside the alternator are six transistor-type rectifier diodes changing generated three-phase a.c. to d.c. for battery charging. The diodes also block current flow from battery to alternator when the engine

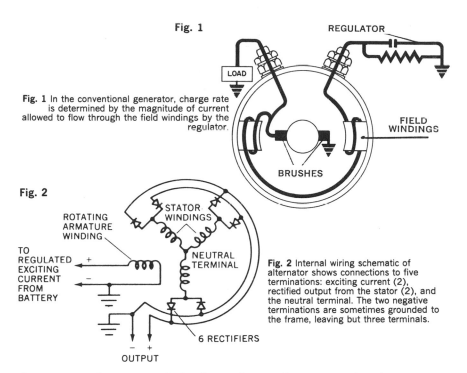

Fig. 1

REGULATOR

LOAD

Fig. 1 In the conventional generator, charge rate is determined by the magnitude of current allowed to flow through the field windings by the regulator.

FIELD WINDINGS

BRUSHES

Fig. 2

ROTATING ARMATURE WINDING

STATOR WINDINGS

TO REGULATED EXCITING CURRENT FROM BATTERY

+

−

NEUTRAL TERMINAL

Fig. 2 Internal wiring schematic of alternator shows connections to five terminations: exciting current (2), rectified output from the stator (2), and the neutral terminal. The two negative terminations are sometimes grounded to the frame, leaving but three terminals.

6 RECTIFIERS

− +
OUTPUT

is stopped. If reverse polarity is applied to the system, the diodes pop like so many blowing fuses, and that's the end of the alternator until it goes to the shop for new diodes.

Output of both alternator and generator must be regulated so charging is at the proper rate. The alternator is regulated by modulation of positive current fed from the battery back to its field terminal. The greater the feedback current, the higher the alternator charges, up to its maximum capability. Function of the voltage regulator is to feed back just the right current to hold system voltage to the desired level.

No reverse-current blocking diode is found in the feedback circuit from battery and regulator to the alternator's field. Therefore, when the engine stops, unless blocked, current would continue flowing to excite the field. Overnight the battery would be discharged through this circuit. To prevent discharge, the feedback circuit is energized through the diesel's fuel cutoff manual key switch or the gas engine's ignition switch. On some diesels, the circuit is energized by an oil or fuel pressure switch. Keep this in mind when shooting troubles.

Unless an oil or fuel pressure switch is used, when the key switch is on, engine stopped, voltage should appear between the alternator's field terminal and ground. This you can measure with a test light.

The conventional generator is regulated by varying the resistance between its field terminal and ground: higher resistance equals lower output. Therefore, if its field terminal is disconnected, the generator will fail to generate; if the field terminal is grounded to the generator's shell, the unit will generate at maximum. Function of the regulator is to automatically adjust the resistance between field terminal and ground, maintaining output voltage at desired level.

The conventional generator's regulator is more complicated than that serving the alternator. The alternator's black box regulates voltage only. But the generator's box regulates not only voltage but reverse current and maximum current as well. Inside the conventional regulator is a reverse-current relay which prevents battery juice from flowing back to the generator when the engine is stopped. Also inside the box is another control limiting the maximum current which the generator can deliver, protecting it against self-destruction.

Since the alternator's internal diodes prevent reverse-current flow, no reverse-current relay is needed in its regulator. And no current limiter is required either because the alternator is inherently self-limiting. So, as you can see, the alternator's regulator is simpler than that modulating the generator. Keep this in mind when trouble-shooting. However, when your trouble-shooting procedures lead you to suspect the regulator, by far the best bet is to simply replace it as a unit. Adjusting and servicing the regulator is a delicate job, one best carried out in a shop having the required equipment. For this reason, one of the most sensible spares you can carry aboard, well wrapped and protected, is an extra regulator. If you suspect that the existing unit is malfunctioning, simply substitute the spare.

Likewise, the sailor who cruises extensively offshore, far from home base, does well to carry a complete, tested, fresh generator or alternator as a major spare part. With it he should carry the fresh V-belt used as its drive.

For start-up, the conventional generator depends upon residual magnetism, a small trace of permanent magnetism in its electromag-

Fig. 3

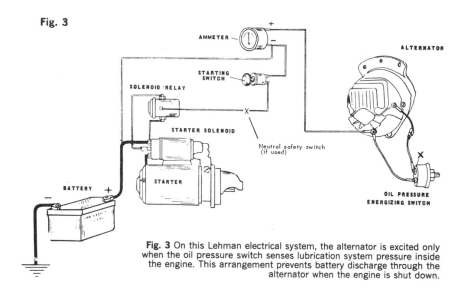

Fig. 3 On this Lehman electrical system, the alternator is excited only when the oil pressure switch senses lubrication system pressure inside the engine. This arrangement prevents battery discharge through the alternator when the engine is shut down.

netic poles. As soon as it starts to rotate, the generator's armature "feels" the residual magnetism, and starts to amplify it, getting the unit into operation. Occasionally, after an engine has been laid up for several months, a generator will lose its residual magnetism and will refuse to put out. In other instances, where a battery has been momentarily installed with reversed polarity, the generator's residual will also be reversed. Then, when operated, it will generate backward, discharging rather than charging the battery.

If your generator loses residual or suffers from reversed polarity, you must "flash the field." This is easy. Simply touch a length of heavy insulated wire between the battery positive terminal and the generator's main output terminal. Momentary contact is sufficient; the rapid surge of current will flash the field in the correct polarity. Then you can start the engine and try the system. Don't leave the wire in contact more than a second or so: Long contact may heat the wire and burn your hands.

Since the alternator is excited by a small flow of current *from* the battery, it will not start to generate *into* an absolutely dead battery. Rarely, indeed, is the battery so flat-out dead that it will not tickle the alternator into action. However, should you run into this unusual situation in an emergency, you can bail yourself out by using a lantern battery, or even some flashlight batteries in series, connected with positive battery terminal to the alternator's field terminal, the battery negative terminal connected to ground. Make your connections with the engine running. After a minute or so, the alternator should have poured enough juice into the system to allow normal, self-sustaining operation.

Neither generator nor alternator should be operated unless connected to a battery. If a circuit breaker is installed in the output circuit, between alternator and battery, the breaker must be of the two-pole common-trip variety. On detecting current higher than its trip point, it must open both charging and exciter circuits. Likewise, any switch in the circuit (such as a battery master switch) must open both circuits simultaneously. If it does not, the alternator may be damaged.

Sometimes when you're trouble-shooting an alternator which does not seem to be charging, you'll wonder whether the alternator or regulator is at fault. A quick way to eliminate the regulator from the picture is this: Touch a wire directly between the battery's positive terminal post and the alternator's field connection, with engine at fast idle. This should excite the alternator to its maximum, making it generate heavily, and pointing the finger of guilt toward the regulator. Don't leave the jumper in place more than a short time or you'll overwork the alternator.

A similar trick can be played with the conventional generator, telling whether it or its regulator is malfunctioning: With engine idling fast, touch a short wire jumper between the field terminal and the generator's shell. If the unit is good, it should start charging—again pointing the finger of guilt toward a malfunctioning regulator.

Virtually all alternators and generators are driven by V-belts. Since the charging accessory soaks up considerable power when working hard, it's important that you maintain the belt well tensioned and that you replace it yearly. Also, always carry a spare belt. Then, if one shreds, you'll be able to make repairs without panic.

Perhaps you plan to add an additional big alternator to your little auxiliary engine. How much power will the alternator demand? How much will it subtract from the power available for propulsion? Considering belt, windage, mechanical and electrical losses, a conserva-

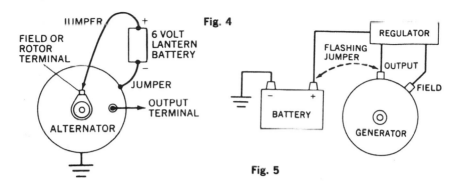

Fig. 4

Fig. 5

Fig. 4 If the boat's storage battery is absolutely dead, it has insufficient power to excite the alternator. A jury rig, using a lantern battery, can bring life to the alternator, restoring the charging system, and allowing it to bootstrap itself back to normal. **Fig. 5** After a conventional generator has been laid up, or if it was inadvertently connected with reverse polarity, its field may require revitalizing. It can be flashed with a heavy conductor jumper as shown.

Fig. 6 Master switch must be ganged with an auxiliary switch so that when the master is opened, the auxiliary will open the circuit to alternator or generator control circuit.

Fig. 6

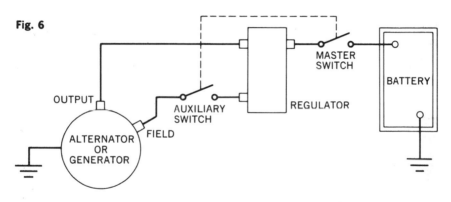

Fig. 7

Fig. 7 V-belt tension is right when thumb pressure deflects belt about as shown. A loose belt slips and wears fast, whereas an overtight belt is rough on pump and generator bearings.

121

tive rule of thumb is two hp. for each 1,000 watts. Therefore, on a nominal 12-volt system, a 40-amp, 14-volt alternator will require one horsepower, and a 60 amp job, a little over 1.5 hp. Both examples are predicated on the alternator working at full strength. Naturally, when load falls, the required power is reduced. Nevertheless, generating load is something to consider when you are specifying the size of an auxiliary and the number of alternators it must drive.

Wired as shown in Fig. 3, the ammeter measures current flowing from alternator or generator to battery. The instrument also registers current flowing from battery to various loads, but not starter current, since that is too heavy for the meter to handle.

The ammeter on your boat indicates net charge to the battery. For example, if accessories are drawing 20-amps, but the ammeter shows 5-amps charge, the alternator is furnishing 25-amps.

Normal instrument response is for the ammeter to show a substantial charge for an interval after the engine has been started. This indicates that the battery is being heavily charged, restoring energy used in cranking the engine. Soon the meter should settle down, and on a long run under power, it will usually indicate but a few amperes charge, if the voltage regulator is functioning properly.

Shooting Alternator Troubles

Screaming during acceleration: The V-belt is loose or has deteriorated, or both. Tighten or replace it.

Constant growling: The ball bearing on the pulley end of the shaft is defective. Have it replaced.

Alternator refuses to charge: Loose V-belt, defective brushes or slip rings inside alternator, defective regulator, blown rectifier diodes, open field circuit to regulator, open circuit between alternator and battery, open circuit between regulator and ignition or diesel cut off key circuit.

Unsteady, irregular charge: Loose V-belt, poor connections, one diode rectifier blown, loose mounting hardware and poor ground connection.

Excessively high charging rate: Defective regulator.

XIII

Engine Starters

The starter is a small, powerful, electric motor and a set of gears arranged to crank the engine when you hit the starting switch. The assembly is small and rugged, delivering tremendous power for a short time. But the starter motor is not designed for continous duty. It tires easily, and if used for extended periods of cranking, will overheat and may burn out.

Keep that in mind when thrashing through a hard-start episode. Don't grind the starter until it gasps for breath and develops a fever. The proper way to crank is to operate the starter for perhaps five seconds, no more. Then pause for 10 or 15 seconds, allowing the starter windings to cool. Following the pause, try again for five seconds. After following this sequence several times, if the engine does not catch, you know full well something is out of whack, and you should take corrective action before you exhaust the battery or roast the starter.

Running free, no load, a starter motor will spin something like 5,000 rpm. Under the load of cranking its engine, it will rotate on the order of 1,000 rpm, a small diesel starter generating some three hp. That's a lot of beef in a small package. Since the starter is capable of cranking the auxiliary at only 100 to 300 rpm., there must be a reduction gear between the starter's armature and the engine. Such reduction is provided by the drive mechanism, which, like all machinery, is a potential source of trouble.

Two kinds of drives are seen on auxiliary inboards: *helical shaft* and *shifter fork* types. Both function in conjunction with a ring gear on the engine flywheel, each meshing a small gear or pinion mounted on the starter's shaft with the large gear which encircles the engine's flywheel. Since the tiny pinion drives the big ring gear, great speed reduction is effected.

The helical shaft drive, called a "Bendix drive," functions by inertia. The starter's pinion floats on a spiral shaft integral with the starter motor. The pinion is small but heavy, so that when the electric motor is energized and the motor accelerates suddenly, the pinion remains rotationally at rest for a split second. Since it is at rest, but the spiral shaft on which it sits is spinning, the pinion is screwed forward until it meshes with the flywheel ring gear. Once meshed, it rotates the flywheel. When the engine fires, the flywheel speeds faster than pinion speed, immediately kicking the little gear back out of mesh.

Between helical shaft and motor armature is a heavy spring, the purpose of which is to absorb the shock ensuing when the pinion crashes into the ring gear. Should this spring ever break, which it does on occasion, the starter is useless. For the man who enjoys extended off-shore cruising, carrying a spare starter drive is not a bad idea.

Another trouble sometimes found in the Bendix drive is sticking of the pinion due to rusting of the spiral shaft. A third though rarer trouble is jamming of the starter gear against the flywheel's ring gear as the two engage. Pinion sticking because of rust can be cured by a squirt of penetrating oil applied to the shaft. On some engines, you must remove the starter from the engine in order to oil the shaft. Don't use heavy grease, it may be self-defeating, making the gear stick in cold weather. When the pinion jams against the flywheel gear, stalling the starter, the usual method of clearing the trouble is to unbolt the starter assembly, then re-install. Should you ever have to do this, inspect the pinion before putting the starter back. If the teeth on the small gear appear worn or deformed, replace the gear as soon as possible. Deformation or chipping of teeth invites jamming.

Virtually all diesels and many modern gasoline auxiliaries use the shifter fork starter drive. Actuated by a powerful electromagnet mounted atop the starter motor, the shifter fork positively meshes the starter pinion with the flywheel ring gear before the starting motor is energized. The arrangement offers the advantage that there

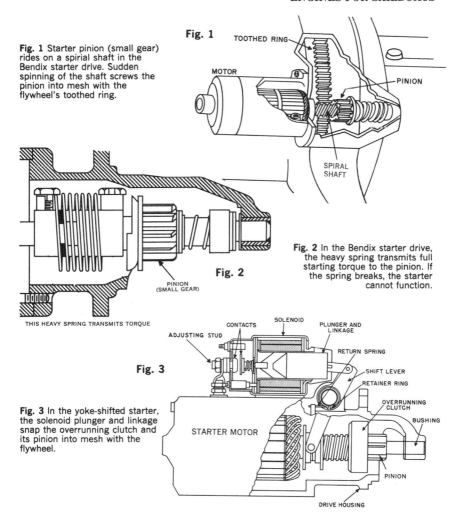

Fig. 1 Starter pinion (small gear) rides on a spirial shaft in the Bendix starter drive. Sudden spinning of the shaft screws the pinion into mesh with the flywheel's toothed ring.

Fig. 2 In the Bendix starter drive, the heavy spring transmits full starting torque to the pinion. If the spring breaks, the starter cannot function.

Fig. 3 In the yoke-shifted starter, the solenoid plunger and linkage snap the overrunning clutch and its pinion into mesh with the flywheel.

is less clash and crash of gears. Particularly on the diesel, which is hard to crank, the shifter fork type is more reliable.

The pinion is carried by the motor shaft extension, the extension being splined. This allows the pinion to slide back and forth while spinning and transmitting torque. Integral with the sliding pinion gear is an overrunning clutch which prevents the engine from driving the starter after the former fires. Also included in the drive is a spring which helps snap the little gear forward when the yoke pushes it. However, unlike the heavy spring in the helical shaft drive, this spring carries no torque and is much less likely to cause trouble.

Mounted on top of the starter motor and looking like a round tin can is the powerful electromagnet which activates the yoke to engage the drive gear. It's called "the solenoid" by mechanics. Not only does the solenoid assembly move a plunger to operate the shifter fork, it also serves as a high-ampacity switch energizing the starter motor. Keep that in mind when trouble-shooting. On gasoline auxiliary engines, the solenoid sometimes performs the third function of directly energizing the ignition coil, bypassing the ballast resistor, increasing ignition voltage during the cranking period.

Where you see four conductors connected to the solenoid on your engine, they are probably the following:

1. Heavy cable from the battery
2. Short, heavy conductor (strap or cable) to starter motor
3. Medium-weight wire from starter switch at the helm
4. Lighter gauge wire connected to ignition coil on gasoline engines.

When you hit the starter switch at the helm position, here's what happens if all goes according to Hoyle:

The electromagnet advances against spring restraint, moving the pinion gear, via the yoke, into mesh with the flywheel ring gear. Continuing its advance after the gears mesh, the plunger next closes the heavy duty switch which energizes the starter motor. Simultaneously, on some gas engines, a switch is closed which increases voltage to the ignition coil.

The solenoid which we've described demands lots of current. Therefore, in some installations it is fed from a heavy duty relay or contactor. Purpose of the contactor is to relieve the manual starter switch and its associated wiring from carrying heavy current. The arrangement is shown in the accompanying drawing. (Unfortunately, to confuse matters, the contactor is also called a "solenoid" by some mechanics.)

Many modern auxiliary engines, both diesel and gasoline, incorporate a neutral-start-only switch in the starting circuit. Wired as shown in Fig. 8 it prevents the engine from being started unless the transmission is in neutral. When either forward or reverse is selected by the helmsman, the start circuit cannot be energized.

Common troubles in yoke-shifted starters are: rust preventing the

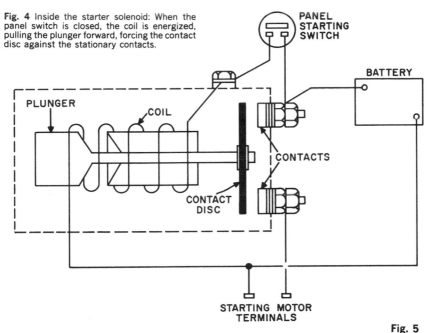

Fig. 4 Inside the starter solenoid: When the panel switch is closed, the coil is energized, pulling the plunger forward, forcing the contact disc against the stationary contacts.

PANEL STARTING SWITCH

BATTERY

PLUNGER

COIL

CONTACTS

CONTACT DISC

STARTING MOTOR TERMINALS

Fig. 5

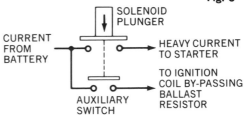

Fig. 5 In some gasoline engine starter solenoids, an auxiliary switch functions to by-pass the ballast resistor, thereby increasing starting voltage to the ignition coil. **Fig. 6** Heavy starting current is carried only by the battery cables and ground circuit. Ignition and push button switch conduct only the current required by the solenoid.

SOLENOID PLUNGER

CURRENT FROM BATTERY

HEAVY CURRENT TO STARTER

TO IGNITION COIL BY-PASSING BALLAST RESISTOR

AUXILIARY SWITCH

Fig. 6

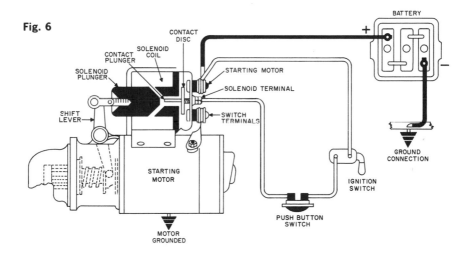

CONTACT DISC

CONTACT PLUNGER

SOLENOID COIL

SOLENOID PLUNGER

BATTERY

STARTING MOTOR

SOLENOID TERMINAL

SWITCH TERMINALS

SHIFT LEVER

STARTING MOTOR

GROUND CONNECTION

IGNITION SWITCH

PUSH BUTTON SWITCH

MOTOR GROUNDED

127

pinion from advancing on its splined shaft, fractured overrunning clutch, defective motor switch, and burned open solenoid coil.

The starter's hunger for amperes leads to many of its troubles. Whereas a 12-volt light bulb may draw one amp, bilge pump five amps, and a battery-operated refrigerator 20, starters commonly demand from 100 to 600 amps, diesel starters being in the upper echelons. Because current is so terrific, even the slightest impediment to electrical flow (resistance) cuts down on starter performance appreciably. Since the starter's mounting flange is its negative electrical connection, that surface and the one to which it mates must be clean metal. Starter cables must be heavy and short, terminations clean, bright, and free of corrosion. Diesels should be served by batteries specifically designed to furnish the unholy currents demanded by their starters.

Shooting Starter Troubles

Starter is dead; will not try to crank the engine. Investigate the following:

1. Dead battery. Connect a 12-volt test light directly across the battery terminal posts. Connect to the *posts,* not the cable clamps. If the light does not glow, the battery is absolutely dead. But suppose the light does go on? Hit the starter switch. If the light remains burning, the battery is probably OK. However, if it goes out or becomes very dim, possibly the battery is sick. Test it with a hydrometer. Charge it before trying another start—and check its electrolyte level.

2. If the battery appears to be OK, connect the test light between the cable termination on the starter assembly and the engine block (ground). If the light goes out when you hit the starter switch, there is probably a high-resistance connection in one of the cables. Disconnect them, cleaning battery posts, cable clamps, and cable terminations at the starter.

3. Still no action? Perhaps the trouble is in the manual starter switch circuit, the one which energizes the solenoid. Connect your test light between ground and the manual switch connection on the solenoid. Hit the starter switch. The light should come on. If it does not, trace through the switch circuit until you find the break.

A possible culprit is the start-in-neutral-only switch mounted on

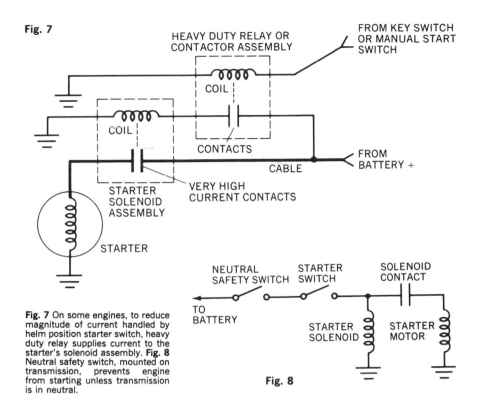

Fig. 7

Fig. 7 On some engines, to reduce magnitude of current handled by helm position starter switch, heavy duty relay supplies current to the starter's solenoid assembly. **Fig. 8** Neutral safety switch, mounted on transmission, prevents engine from starting unless transmission is in neutral.

Fig. 8

or near the transmission. Unless this switch closes properly, the solenoid cannot be energized, and the engine will not start. When this switch operates properly, transmission in neutral, a test light connected across its terminals will not glow when the manual starter switch is closed.

Starter solenoid clicks, but starter motor does not operate. The switch inside the solenoid is probably defective. Connect your test light between ground and the downstream (starter motor) side of the solenoid. Hit the manual starter switch. The light should glow. If it does not, you've found the trouble: The solenoid is sick.

Solenoid clacks and chatters; engine does not crank. Most common cause of this syndrome is a badly discharged battery. Second most possible cause is poor battery connections or a very badly frayed battery cable. Here's what happens: There is sufficient voltage to pull in the solenoid plunger. But when the plunger switch makes contact to the load, potential falls so low that the solenoid feels insufficient voltage to hang in. It releases: voltage rises, pulling it in again, back and forth ad infinitum, like a buzzer.

Starter cranks slowly. Most probable cause is a partially discharged battery. Test the cells with a hydrometer. Charge the battery. Other causes are overly viscous crankcase oil in cool weather, corroded or frayed cables in any weather.

Starter cranks engine smartly for about a half turn, then stops abruptly. If the unit is the spiral shaft drive type, there is a possibility that the starter pinion has jammed against the flywheel ring gear, as described earlier. Regardless of starter type, there is the dim possibility that a cylinder has been flooded with water because of back-flooding from the exhaust system or because of an internal fault. Most common internal fault is a ruptured head gasket.

A cylinder partially filled with water blocks its piston as the piston rises. The water acts as a hydrostatic lock, blocking engine rotation. If you suspect that your engine suffers from this malady, remove the spark plugs or fuel injectors. Then hit the starter. If the engine rotates and water spits from one or more cylinders, you've a major trouble and the engine needs professional help, either internally or on its exhaust system.

XIV

Sailboat
Exhaust Systems

Because sailboat auxiliary engines are very close to the waterline or even below it, their exhaust systems require more careful planning than those on motorboats. This is so because in virtually all installations, the exhaust pipes carry cooling water. On the powerboat where the engine is well above the waterline, it's easy to provide a comfortable downward slope of pipe from manifold to transom. But it's obviously difficult to slope downward when the engine is already low in the bilge.

It's true that spent cooling water could be conveniently pumped overboard via any kind of conduit. But in practice it is directed through the exhaust pipes to cool them. Water cooling of the exhaust is an essential part of any auxiliary installation, and while it complicates running of the pipes, it's a necessary evil. An un-cooled exhaust would pose a dangerous fire hazard.

The reason the exhaust pipe must slope downhill all the way, or have some kind of trap, is to prevent cooling water from flowing back into the exhaust manifold when the engine is shut down. Auxiliaries have been ruined by faulty exhaust installations which allowed water to sneak back into the engine. Not only does the water cause rust, but it may instigate hydrostatic lock, blocking piston travel by incompressible liquid. Water hammer will damage the engine mechanically when an attempt is made to start it.

Exhaust piping or tubing should have a continous downward pitch of at least ½" per foot, measured when the boat is at rest. Where this magnitude of pitch cannot be realized, the exhaust must be fitted with artificial means of getting the water out of the tailpipe. The accompanying drawings show several common arrangements.

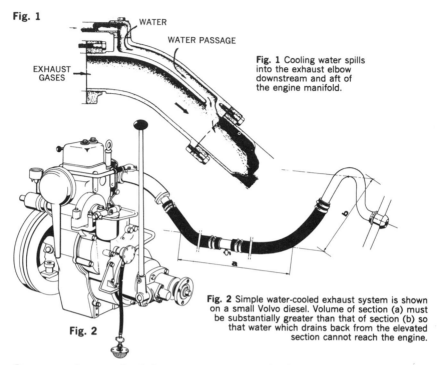

Fig. 1

WATER

WATER PASSAGE

EXHAUST GASES

Fig. 1 Cooling water spills into the exhaust elbow downstream and aft of the engine manifold.

Fig. 2 Simple water-cooled exhaust system is shown on a small Volvo diesel. Volume of section (a) must be substantially greater than that of section (b) so that water which drains back from the elevated section cannot reach the engine.

Fig. 2

One popular method is to use a water-jacketed exhaust riser as shown in Fig. 1. Spent engine cooling water is pumped into the jacketed riser. At a point following the upper loop, the water is dumped back into the exhaust where it cools the remainder of the run to the transom. A modification of this is to run the water jacket the entire length, never mixing water and exhaust gas directly.

Fig. 4 shows an exhaust system which is increasing in popularity because of its simplicity and effectiveness. Ideal for engines below the waterline, the system uses a "Hydro-Hush" or pot type muffler which handles both exhaust gas and water. Spend water is injected into the hot exhaust gases in a steeply sloping section of pipe close to the engine. Usually located just aft or to one side of the auxiliary, the pot-type muffler accepts the mixture of gas and water, ejecting it to the tail pipe by exhaust pressure. When the engine is shut down, the trace of water in the pipe between pot and transom is trapped in the pot and prevented from flowing back to the engine. Among the simplest and lightest of systems, it works well and creates negligible back pressure. It also does a nice job of quieting the exhaust.

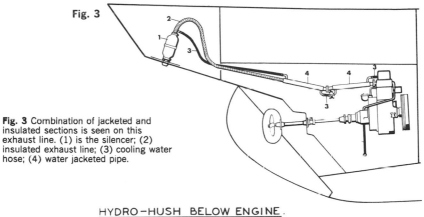

Fig. 3

Fig. 3 Combination of jacketed and insulated sections is seen on this exhaust line. (1) is the silencer; (2) insulated exhaust line; (3) cooling water hose; (4) water jacketed pipe.

HYDRO—HUSH BELOW ENGINE.

Fig. 4

Fig. 4 Lightweight pot-type stainless steel muffler silences exhaust noise while pumping cooling water overboard from auxiliaries below the waterline. U-tube and vent prevent water from sneaking in through cooling water pump and flooding exhaust when engine is shut down.
Fig. 5 Onan's Aqualift marine muffler can be used on below-waterline auxiliary engines or powered generator sets. Like other pot type mufflers, it lifts spent cooling water above the boat's waterline, spewing the coolant overboard, mixed with exhaust gases.

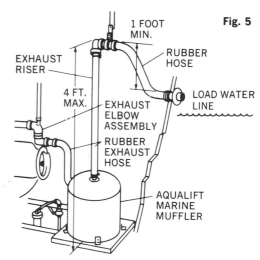

Fig. 5

133

Exhaust piping, tubing, and hose should be of a diameter equal to or greater than the diameter of the outlet from the manifold. The system should have as few bends as possible, and what bends are necessary should be of ample radius. The idea here is to minimize back pressure on the engine. Excess back pressure reduces power, generates unwanted heat on the exhaust valves, and may damage other parts of the engine. Pressure equal to 39" of water is the maximum for many engines, and is the pressure given specifically for Westerbeke diesels.

Most auxiliary installations are such that the back pressure is well below the 39" of water figure. However, if you have reason to suspect the pressure in your system, you might like to measure it. This you can do with a few feet of Tygon or other transparent tubing as shown in Fig. 6. Tap the tubing into the exhaust pipe close to the engine. Form a section into a U-tube partially filled with water. Run the engine at full throttle and load. Measurement "A" on the sketch must not exceed 39". (This is equal to approximately 0.75 pounds per square inch.)

On most auxiliary installations, all the spent seawater is directed through exhaust tubing to provide adequate cooling. Required flow is not terribly great. The American Boat & Yacht Council states that water volume in gallons per minute should equal $GPM = \frac{displ \times rpm}{666,000}$. Displacement is expressed in cubic inches. According to this, if your auxiliary displaces 220 cubic inches and operates at 3,000 rpm. full throttle, one gallon of water per minute should be sufficient to cool the exhaust. You might like to test your engine's flow, using a bucket to catch the water flowing from the exhaust, and applying the formula to determine if the flow is sufficient. It's likely to be OK.

What if the water should stop flowing through the exhaust while you're underway and no one notices? The thing will overheat, and that could be embarrassing, or even dangerous. For this reason you can consider rigging an over-temperature alarm in the system, preferably in the muffler. Wired as shown in Fig. 7, it will sound the alarm when temperature exceeds its set-point.

You've probably been aboard a boat proceeding downwind under power and have gotten a snoot full of exhaust fumes. Nauseating, particularly on a hot day. One way to minimize the volume of vapors

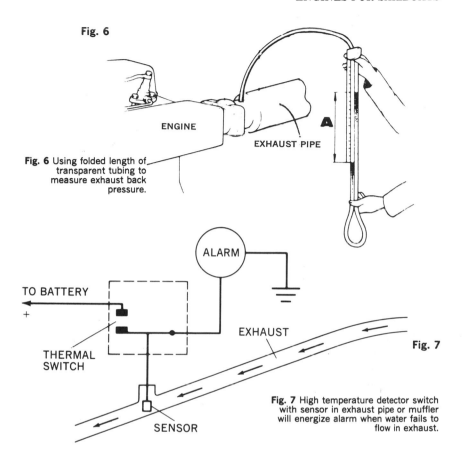

Fig. 6

ENGINE

EXHAUST PIPE

A

Fig. 6 Using folded length of transparent tubing to measure exhaust back pressure.

ALARM

TO BATTERY

+

EXHAUST

Fig. 7

THERMAL SWITCH

SENSOR

Fig. 7 High temperature detector switch with sensor in exhaust pipe or muffler will energize alarm when water fails to flow in exhaust.

drifting into the cockpit is to offset the exhaust pipe, having it terminate well to one side of the transom or out the side of the boat well above the waterline. A difficulty in having it on the side is that it may be submerged when the boat heels, and you don't want that. Best compromise, then, is offset to one side of the counter, perhaps with a deflector to throw the expelled noxious gases outward.

A muffler in the exhaust system reduces the racket and is a desirable accessory. Naturally, it should be of true marine design, able to handle cooling water, and of non-corroding material. Good lightweight mufflers are available in Monel and stainless steel. In silencing the racket, you need not install one of those enormous cast iron monstrosties which weigh the stern down.

Numerous metallic and non-metallic materials are suitable for use in wet exhaust systems. Those approved by ABYC for use as diesel exhaust carriers in a wet system, in order of preference are:

Nickel-Iron Chrome

70% nickel-30% copper

Copper-Nickel alloys

Approved types of fiberglass tubing certified for marine use

Rubber hose approved for the purpose

Copper is a poor material for diesel exhaust because products of combustion attack it. Galvanized steel or iron pipe is borderline, having limited life in diesel exhaust service.

Approved materials for wet gasoline engine exhaust, in order of preference are:

Nickel-Iron-Chrome

70% Nickel-30% Copper

Copper-Nickel alloys

Fiberglass, marine certified

Rubber hose

Brass pipe or copper tubing

Note that copper and brass don't rate too highly, even though they are frequently used. Enameled or galvanized iron or steel pipe are acceptable, but their longevity is limited.

Where sections of rubber exhaust hose are used in the system, as is common, each junction should be clamped with two stainless steel clamps spaced about a half inch apart and a half inch from the end of the hose. The entire run of pipe and tube must be well supported and free of low sag points which will trap water. Once a season, at least, flashlight in hand, you should scramble about the engine compartment and aft to the transom, inspecting the system and assuring yourself that it is tight, shipshape, and secure. Little other maintenance is required except when the boat is laid up for the winter. Then, the muffler should be drained or removed and dumped out so that water does not freeze inside and burst its seams. (See Chapter XVI for details.)

XV

The Power Train

This chapter covers the transmission or lower unit, reduction gears, shafting, stuffing box, shaft brake, and propeller. These are the principal components comprising the auxiliary's power train.

Transmission

Primary rules for preventing transmission trouble are simply to keep it lubed, keep it dry, and keep its attached controls in good working order. There's also a secondary rule: Don't strain it beyond capacity or abuse it. Severe strain you will surely throw on the transmission if you wrap up a lobster pot or somebody's mooring line and then persist in pouring on the power, trying to break the snarl. This can burn the transmission's clutch plates and demolish its insides.

You will surely abuse the transmission if you insist on throwing it in and out of gear with the engine at high speed. Another way to test its temper is to throw it into reverse directly from forward at high revolutions. Obviously, if you have to perform a violent maneuver once in an emergency, it won't kill the transmission. But if you persist in shifting at high speed as standard operating procedure, you will indeed deep six the device.

Now, if you *should* strain the transmission beyond its capacity forcing it to slip its clutch, keep eye and ear cocked in its direction for a while thereafter. If you detect that it slips, if the boat seems to go slower at your usual revolutions, or if the transmission overheats, its clutch plates are probably worn, and the unit should be removed for overhaul. On many auxiliary installations this is not as terrible a job as it might seem at first blush. Provided there is room to unbolt the transmission and move it aft about 2", it can be removed from

Fig. 1

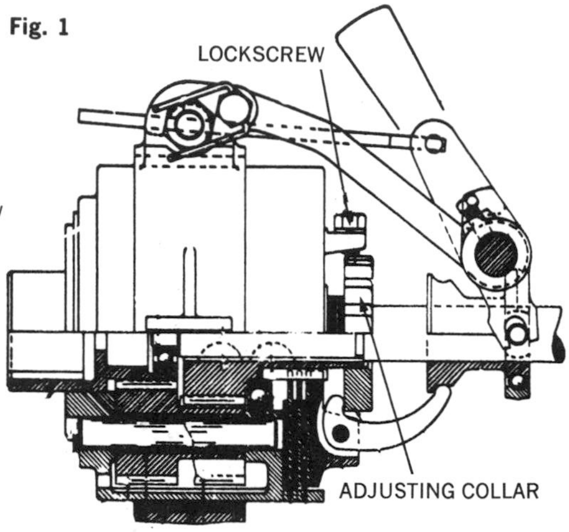

LOCKSCREW

Fig. 1 Manual transmission is simple
to adjust. When gear slips in forward
drive, lockscrew is loosened, and
adjusting collar screwed inward a few
notches. Illustrated transmission is
from an Atomic-4 auxiliary.

ADJUSTING COLLAR

the boat without disturbing the engine.

In a qualified transmission shop, the unit can be overhauled in a day or two. It is not a job, however, that should be tackled by just any local, friendly mechanic. Special tools, parts and fixtures are required to do the job Bristol fashion. We are thinking in particular of the popular Warner and Paragon hydraulic transmissions used on so many auxiliary diesels and gasoline engines. These do not incorporate adjustable clutch assemblies.

Manual transmissions such as those used on the Atomic-Four have adjustments for both the forward clutch and reverse bands. If the gear slips when in forward drive, tighten the adjusting collar sufficient to eliminate the slip. If the unit slips in reverse, tighten the brake band adjusting nut enough to make the clutch hold. With transmission cover removed, the adjustments are easy to make, requiring only the simplest hand tools.

Keeping the transmission lubricated is easy: Every couple of weeks, pull its dipstick and check the oil level. Always do this with the boat quiet in the water and engine shut down. If the dipstick indicates the need for oil, top her up, using the proper liquid. On most American transmissions and reduction gears, automobile transmission fluid Type A is used. However, find out what oil is recommended before you add fresh lube.

Suppose you're offshore and Murphy's Law takes command: A

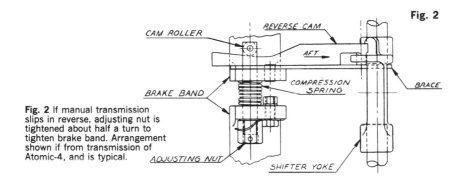

Fig. 2

CAM ROLLER

REVERSE CAM

AFT

COMPRESSION SPRING

BRACE

BRAKE BAND

Fig. 2 If manual transmission slips in reverse, adjusting nut is tightened about half a turn to tighten brake band. Arrangement shown if from transmission of Atomic-4, and is typical.

ADJUSTING NUT

SHIFTER YOKE

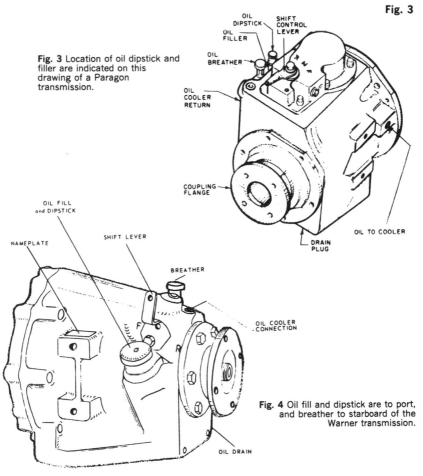

Fig. 3

Fig. 3 Location of oil dipstick and filler are indicated on this drawing of a Paragon transmission.

OIL DIPSTICK

SHIFT CONTROL LEVER

OIL FILLER

OIL BREATHER

OIL COOLER RETURN

COUPLING FLANGE

OIL TO COOLER

DRAIN PLUG

OIL FILL and DIPSTICK

NAMEPLATE

SHIFT LEVER

BREATHER

OIL COOLER CONNECTION

Fig. 4 Oil fill and dipstick are to port, and breather to starboard of the Warner transmission.

OIL DRAIN

Fig. 4

139

flexible hose connecting transmission to cooler ruptures. Whoosh - out comes the transmission fluid, messing up the bilge and putting the gearbox out of action. You manage to improvise a way to block the leaking oil line, but what to do for transmission fluid on which to limp home?

Use engine oil. It'll work; it will not damage the transmission, and it will fill the bill until you can get to port and make permanent repairs. Then you will replace the engine oil with the right stuff.

Moral of that tale, incidentally, is that you should not only carry extra engine oil aboard at all times, but should also carry a few quarts of transmission fluid. Cheap insurance.

Keeping the transmission dry involves nothing more than maintaining bilgewater level below the gearbox's breather, which is on top. But what to do if your boat takes on more than her alloted share of bilge water, submerging the transmission?

No great sweat. After your bilge pumping operations, use a little hand pump like the PAR Utility, and suck all the oil out of the transmission. Refill the unit with fresh lube; run the engine a few minutes; shut down, then check lube level again, topping up if necessary. It's not a bad idea, incidentally, to change the transmission oil once a year. Good preventive maintenance, helping keep the inside dry.

A few engines use transmissions which are lubricated directly by the same oil that serves the engine crankcase. Obviously, on these auxiliaries, such as the popular Atomic-four, periodic transmission lubrication service is not required. But the engine's crankcase should be serviced regularly, of course.

Whether the transmission is hydraulically or manually shifted, it must have positive-acting controls between the helm position and engine. Cables and linkage must have more travel than required to fully move the transmission shift lever full forward and aft. In addition, control linkages to manually-shifted transmissions must be tough, positive, and strong, so that when you horse the lever at the helm position into reverse, the lever on the transmission will feel the full thrust of your command. More than one transmission has failed because of being fitted with sloppy acting controls. If you have any doubt about those on your yacht, inspect them, possibly revamping

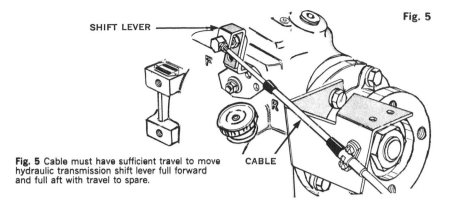

SHIFT LEVER

Fig. 5

CABLE

Fig. 5 Cable must have sufficient travel to move hydraulic transmission shift lever full forward and full aft with travel to spare.

the arrangement if you doubt its effectiveness.

Many transmissions, particularly those with reduction gears, are fitted with an external water-cooled oil cooler. A pair of small diameter pipes or hoses carries oil from transmission to cooler and return. Larger hoses conduct water through the cooler, which is a heat exchanger. Maintain these hoses and tubes in good condition, keeping them well fastened. If one of the oil hoses breaks, out will come the transmission fluid, and you'll go dead in the water. Worse, if one of the water hoses ruptures, water will pour forth in great volume. If the installation is below the waterline, a ruptured hose could sink your boat.

Some transmission oil coolers incorporate a zinc pencil screwed into the water chamber to reduce corrosion. Change this pencil once a year. That's good preventive maintenance.

Whether or not the cooler has a zinc pencil, make sure it is well grounded to the engine or transmission housing so there is actual electrical contact from the cooler, through its bracket, to the casting. Electrical contact helps the zinc in the cooler protect nearby associated parts on the engine. Alternatively, if the cooler lacks a zinc, proper contact allows the zinc pencil on the base engine to protect the cooler. Often, when engine manufacturers mount the cooler, they neglect to scrape paint off the mounting bracket; you should do this yourself, assuring decent contact.

Why Reduction Gears?

At first blush it might appear that the faster a boat's prop spins, the faster the boat will go. Not so. A big, slow-rotating wheel pro-

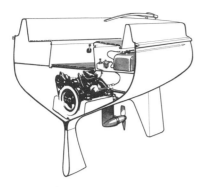

Fig. 6

Fig. 6 Volvo sailboat outdrive installed so that propeller stream flows over the spade rudder.

vides more push than a small high-speed one, the larger prop moving the sailboat's displacement hull more smartly than the small screw. That's why many auxiliary engines are fitted with reduction gears.

A gearbox allows the small engine to rev fast, developing its full power. Simultaneously, the gears turn the propeller slowly, permitting it to be of ample proportions to develop the considerable thrust required to push a displacement hull. Outboard motors also have reduction gears in their lower units, and motors intended specifically for sailboat auxiliary service incorporate greater reductions than those intended for general use. They also have larger propellers. The British Seagull motor, for example, has a wheel so gross that is looks almost like a fan.

Outdrives

The S-drive or Z-drive, used extensively as sterndrive propulsion on power cruisers and runabouts, is increasingly popular on sailboats, albeit in modified form. The sailboat outdrive, perfectly adapted to fin keel boats with spade rudders, passes directly through the bottom of the hull, the hull opening being sealed by a neoprene boot.

Attractive features of the drive are that the rig hugs the bottom of the boat, can be positioned fore and aft relatively without restriction, and is simply installed, no prop shaft or stuffing box being required. In contrast to the outboard, the outdrive throws its prop wash over the rudder, providing good steering and maneuverability; the skipper is able to use his tiller rather than wrestling with an outboard on the transom. Again compared to the outboard, the outdrive has the disadvantage of not being retractable for low-drag

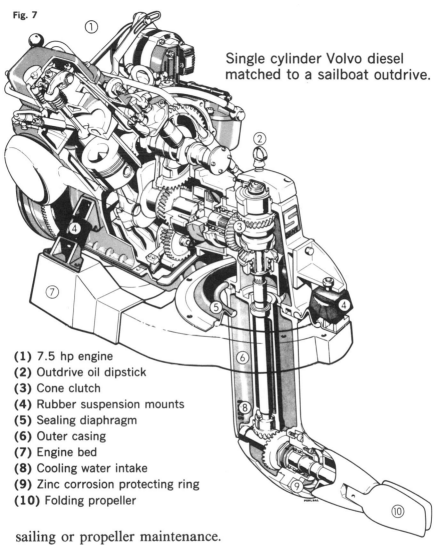

Fig. 7

Single cylinder Volvo diesel
matched to a sailboat outdrive.

(1) 7.5 hp engine
(2) Outdrive oil dipstick
(3) Cone clutch
(4) Rubber suspension mounts
(5) Sealing diaphragm
(6) Outer casing
(7) Engine bed
(8) Cooling water intake
(9) Zinc corrosion protecting ring
(10) Folding propeller

sailing or propeller maintenance.

Outboard Marine offers its OMC Sail Drive, a complete package comprising a two-cylinder, two-cycle motor rated 15 hp. at 3,300 rpm, married to a lower unit with 2:1 reduction gear. Through its three-blade free-wheeling prop, the rig provides 300 pounds of static thrust. This is ample for sailboats up to something like 25 feet. Attractive feature is that the powerhead is one of the company's regular outboard motors, parts for which are available at Johnson and Evinrude dealers.

Volvo Penta markets a through-hull outdrive somewhat similar to the OMC unit. However, Volvo mates its sailboat drive to several small diesels of one and two cylinders, in horsepowers of 7.5, 10, 13, and 23. Nice feature is that the propeller is full feathering, offering little drag when the boat is under sail.

Hydraulic Drives

The hydraulic drive system comprises a diesel or gasoline engine driving a high-pressure oil pump which, in turn, drives a remote hydraulic motor. The hydraulic motor is connected via a short shaft to the boat's propeller. Magnificent flexibility is offered by this arrangement, a popular version of which is manufactured by Volvo. The hydro-drive engine can be located anywhere in the boat, even in the forward sail locker or athwartships aft of the propeller. It's also simple to route additional high-pressure hydraulic hoses for operating powerful winches or electric generators, using energy from the propulsion engine. Because of its versatility, we may see more of this drive in the future.

Prop Shaft

The propeller shaft serving the inboard auxiliary can be of Monel or marine bronze. It should be perfectly straight, naturally, or it will cause vibration and be almost impossible to seal tight with a stuffing box. The shaft should have a zinc collar attached close to the propeller to protect both against corrosion. This is true even in boats sailed in potable water. Corrosion is much slower in fresh water, but nevertheless poses a threat to underwater hardware unless that hardware is protected by an appropriate mass of zinc. In order to function, the zinc blob *must* be in good electrical contact with the metal it is intended to protect.

Sailing Brake

There's an old saw heard around the waterfront which says, "If you sail with the propeller spinning, the transmission will be ruined."

That is not true. The modern transmission is not damaged in being free-wheeled by the propeller as the boat sails. What's more, tests show that the free-spinning prop offers less drag to the boat than the locked one.

Despite the above, most of us like to lock the propeller when

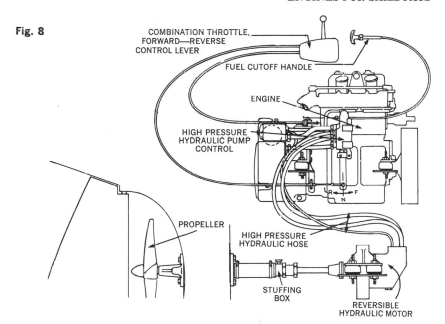

Fig. 8

COMBINATION THROTTLE, FORWARD—REVERSE CONTROL LEVER

FUEL CUTOFF HANDLE

ENGINE

HIGH PRESSURE HYDRAULIC PUMP CONTROL

PROPELLER

HIGH PRESSURE HYDRAULIC HOSE

STUFFING BOX

REVERSIBLE HYDRAULIC MOTOR

Fig. 8 Power is transmitted from engine to propeller via a high pressure hydraulic pump, flexible hoses, and a hydraulic motor. The new hydraulic system allows positioning of the engine almost anywhere on the boat, even far forward.

sailing. A locked propeller is quieter, and the locked shaft cannot be abraded by the stuffing box, neither can the transmission be worn. It's easy to lock the shaft of a transmission having manual shift. You simply place the shift lever "in gear."

However, the hydraulically shifted box is different; placing it in gear does not stop shaft rotation. You've got to apply some kind of brake. Several kinds of brakes are available. A common variety is simply a brake drum on the shaft and a brake band surrounding it. To stop the shaft from spinning, the skipper pulls on a brake handle, tightening the band on the drum and, presto, the spinning ceases.

The simplest brake we've seen is a pair of locking grip pliers pinched on the shaft and blocked against a piece of wood. The arrangement works, but has serious drawbacks. If the engine is started with the "brake" in place, the block of wood goes flying (possibly through the hull) and the locking pliers chew the shaft to a fare thee well.

There's a patented shaft stopper on the market which works quite well and takes very little space. It's comprised of a metal disk attached to the transmission flange coupling, plus a hydraulically actuated plunger which indexes the disk. When the engine runs, transmission fluid pressure moves a piston in the actuator, pulling the plunger away from a detent on the rotating disk and allowing the disk and shaft to rotate. Immediately after the engine stops, spring pressure forces the plunger into the detent, locking the shaft against rotation. The detents are radially spaced so that the shaft always stops with propeller blades aligned vertically behind deadwood.

Where your boat has a 2-blade prop, it's nice to stop the shaft with its blades lined up vertically behind keel and deadwood. Such positioning reduces drag. A dot of bright paint on coupling or shaft will show you the prop's position, helping you apply the brake with the wheel exactly vertical. When the dot is straight up, so is the prop; that's all there is to the contrivance.

Stuffing Box

Purpose of the stuffing box is to allow the prop shaft to rotate freely while preventing water from leaking into the bilge through the shaft hole. Most stuffing boxes have a packed shaft seal and a gland nut which adjusts the pressure forcing the packing against the shaft. The ideal adjustment is that which tightens the seal just sufficient to prevent leaks, but not so tight as to create excessive friction and generate heat. Granted, it's nice to have a dry bilge, but for the sake of shaft longevity it's a good idea to adjust the stuffing box so that an occasional drop of water drips when the boat is under power.

Propellers

The propeller art is one steeped in mystery. Among powerboat men, there is no quicker way to start a warm technical discussion than to broach the subject of propeller selection. Fortunately, however, since most sailors are not keenly interested in milking the last fractional knot from their auxiliaries, the art of prop selection and care is much simplified.

Propeller terms which you'll hear bandied about, and their significance, are as follows:

Diameter is the diameter of a circle swept by the blade's tips. Applied to a two-blade wheel, it is the distance from tip to tip of the blades. A wheel's power-handling capability is determined largely by

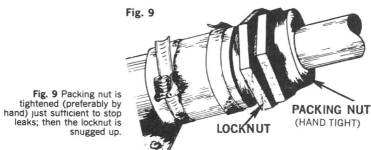

Fig. 9

Fig. 9 Packing nut is tightened (preferably by hand) just sufficient to stop leaks; then the locknut is snugged up.

LOCKNUT

PACKING NUT (HAND TIGHT)

its diameter. A large-diameter prop can handle more power than a small one at the same revolutions; and it takes but a small increase in diameter to greatly increase power-handling ability. Diameter is measured in inches.

Pitch is the the theoretical distance, in inches, which the prop would advance itself through the water in one revolution if the water were solid and there were no slip. A wheel having 12″ pitch would advance one foot for each revolution. At 1,500 rpm. this wheel would advance 1,500 feet per minute or about 17 miles an hour.

A propeller's pitch determines how fast it tries to push the boat at any given number of revolutions per minute. If it tries to propel the displacement sailboat hull faster than the old girl will allow, it slips excessively, makes a fuss, and may cavitate.

Slip is expressed in percentage and is the difference between theoretical propeller advance and actual speed. If theoretical advance is 18 knots and the boat goes 9 knots, slip is 50%.

Rotation is defined as right- or left-hand: A right-hand wheel rotates clockwise when viewed from behind the boat facing forward. A left-hand wheel rotates counterclockwise. It is terribly important that you specify the correct rotation when ordering a prop. Otherwise you'll find yourself in the predicament of the poor sailor who installed the wrong wheel: Starting the auxiliary, he threw the clutch into reverse, only to shoot forward and wallop the pilings.

Cavatation describes the condition wherein the propeller is partially surrounded by air, water vapor, and froth, all of which prevent it from getting a good bite on the water. Cavitation is indicated when the propeller loses pushing power and when there are rumblings, bumblings and strange non-mechanical thumps from the area of the prop. Causes of cavitation include a prop of excessive pitch, mounting of the wheel too close to the surface, location of the wheel too close to deadwood, excessive rpm on a wheel with narrow blades, and weed or bits of rope wrapped on the shaft or wheel hub. If your outboard motor cavitates, lower the prop deeper into the water. This may require a longer unit manufactured specifically for sailboat application. You may also need a propeller having less than standard pitch.

When the yacht is under sail, a dead propeller naturally causes drag, slowing the boat. If you have an outboard auxiliary, it's easy to eliminate the drag completely by tilting up the lower unit. However, with conventional drive or Z-drive, the prop must remain submerged, doing its dirty work. Even so, there are ways to reduce drag:

Where the two-blade wheel is located behind deadwood, you can align it vertically, watching an inside reference mark on the shaft as described earlier.

Select a prop with narrow blades specifically made for sailboat auxiliary use. Such blades are somewhat less efficient than broader ones, but who cares when a wheel is applied to a boat primarily intended for sailing.

Folding and feathering propellers offer a splendid means of providing reasonably efficient propulsion together with reduced drag. One type of wheel automatically folds into a straight line, appearing almost like an extension of the propeller shaft. It offers little sailing drag, but functions indifferently when the engine is reversed. Another version is the controllable-pitch prop: You can change its pitch manually by a lever as the engine operates, and can manually feather it to minimum drag configuration when the engine is shut down. This wheel performs its intended functions well, but is more complicated than the standard variety.

XVI

Laying up the Auxiliary

When the sailing season draws to a close, you inspect your sail inventory, send sails to the sailmaker for repair, and perhaps order a new spinnaker for spring delivery. Carefully, you check out the condition of halyards, reverse or renew the sheets, comb over the ground tackle, and inspect the spars. The boat and its rigging you put to bed with the greatest of care.

But how about the auxiliary? The mechanical breeze requires attention, too.

Left alone, unwinterized, unattended, the diesel or gasoline engine in your bilge can suffer more damage and wear, can deteriorate more than in a dozen seasons of use.

Here's a surprising thought expressed some years ago by a respected marine engineer. He said: "The sole difference between a new engine and one ready for the scrap heap is four pounds of metal." Did you ever think of it in that light? The difference is only four pounds of iron, steel, copper, and babbitt rusted, corroded and abraded away. Be smart, skipper, don't let a big share of that four pounds get eaten out of your auxiliary when you lay the boat up during the off-season.

Even though your boat is professionally hauled or winterized for wet storage, it is a good idea for you to double-check the job yourself. After all, it only takes one freeze-out to ruin an otherwise beautiful $4,000 diesel, and you are the one who has to pay.

Before tackling the decommissioning job, gird yourself for action with a few ordinary hand tools, a pump-type oil can, spray can of rust preventive, fresh fuel and oil filter element, plus a supply of lubricant for transmission and crankcase.

To winterize, proceed as follows:

Before the boat is hauled, change the crankcase oil; this applies to both diesel and gasoline engines. Do it while the boat is afloat, because you must run the engine sufficiently to heat the oil before draining the old lubricant. Pump out or drain the dirty, contaminated lube; you may need a small hand pump like the PAR utility pump to do the job. (And please dispose of the oil properly. Don't dump it into our sailing waters, they're dirty enough already,)

Replace the oil filter, being careful not to dribble oil into the bilge. Then refill the crankcase with the required volume of fresh oil. Following this, run the engine a few minutes to distribute the fresh lube throughout the engine's internals.

You may wonder why it's important to change engine oil when the machine is decommissioned. "Why not wait until fitting-out time?" you may ask.

The purpose of changing oil at lay-up time is to protect the engine against internal rust and corrosion which are induced by acids and moisture in the used oil. Fresh oil protects rather than corrodes the engine during layup, so don't wait until spring to do the job.

If yours is a gasoline engine, shut off the line valve close to the fuel tank. Take the flame arrester off the carburetor. Start the engine; run it on the few ounces of fuel remaining in the carburetor's float bowl. Operate at about 900 rpm. while slowly pouring a cupful of SAE #10 or #20 oil into the carburetor throat. Finally, stall the engine by pouring the last one or two shot glasses of oil into the carburetor rapidly enough to strangle the engine. When she stops, turn off the ignition. What you have done is to burn most of the gasoline in the carburetor. Simultaneously, you've coated the engine's induction system with corrosion-fighting lubricant.

Fogging-off the engine, as described in the previous paragraph, is risky on a diesel. Don't do it. If you pour oil rapidly into the diesel's intake, the oil may act as fuel, burning like crazy in the cylinders and making the engine run away, out of control of its governor. If you like, you can spray a mist of rust inhibitor into the air intake after the engine is shut down, but you'd better not do it while she's running.

Pump or drain all the diesel fuel or gasoline from the fuel tank.

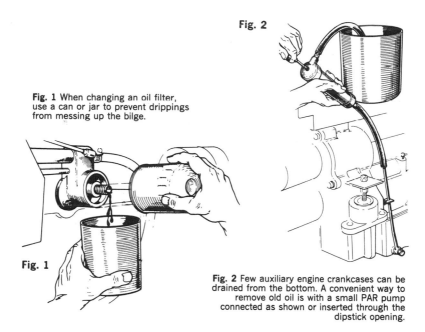

Fig. 2

Fig. 1 When changing an oil filter, use a can or jar to prevent drippings from messing up the bilge.

Fig. 1

Fig. 2 Few auxiliary engine crankcases can be drained from the bottom. A convenient way to remove old oil is with a small PAR pump connected as shown or inserted through the dipstick opening.

This operation will not only lighten the yacht, but will start your next season with fresh fuel. Gasoline or fuel oil which remains in the tanks for a prolonged period becomes stale and sometimes deterioriates. However, if you prefer to leave diesel fuel in the tank during lay-up, add inhibitor. It helps keep the fuel in good condition, and prevents formation of undesirable products inside the tank.

Should you elect to drain your diesel's fuel tank, you will allow unwanted air to enter the supply pipe or siphon tube in the tank. This means that at fitting-out time you must completely bleed the system of air. But of course the art of bleeding the diesel was discussed in Chapter VIII.

After blowing dirt out of their recesses, remove the spark plugs from the gasoline engine. Using a pump-type oil can if necessary, squirt an ounce or so of clean engine oil into each plug boss. To protect the ignition system against high-voltage surges, ground the high voltage lead from the ignition coil by pressing it against engine metal. After this, crank the engine with the starter for a few seconds. Cranking the engine will distribute the lubricant throughout the cylinders, protecting them against rust.

Diesel cylinders can be protected against rust in a similar manner. However, since the diesel has no spark plugs, the oil must be squirted into the cylinder through an injector or glow plug boss. Often, removing these components is harder work than taking out the gasoline engine's spark plug, but it's worth the effort. With glow plug or injector removed, pour a couple of ounces of oil into each cylinder, crank over the engine a dozen revolutions, replace the plug or injector, then don't crank the engine again until it's recommissioned.

A raw water cooling pump having flexible neoprene impeller is used in the cooling systems of many diesel and gasoline auxiliaries. When the engine is decommissioned, standing still for several months, the impeller may take a "set," failing to operate when the engine is recommissioned. The manufacturer, a dealer, mechanic, or your owner's manual will tell if your engine has this type pump. If so, open up the pump and remove the impeller. It's not a difficult job at all. At recommissioning time you can either reinstall the impeller or replace it.

Some new cruising sailboats are fitted with outdrive propulsion, the through-the-hull Z-drive type. Details on exact lay-up procedures vary a little. However what follows her will put you on the right track in protecting your drive against the ravages of the off-season:

1. Drain the drive unit gearcase completely, getting out all the old lube and any possible traces of water. If a lot of water contaminates lower unit oil, the unit very likely needs in-shop repairs. It probably has bad gaskets or seals. Refill the unit with gear lubricant.

2. Remove the drive unit, if required, and lubricate joints, bearings splined shaft and couplings. If this work is beyond the scope of your tools and abilities, have the work done. You certainly don't want the insides of the lower unit to rust and corrode.

3. Remove the propeller and apply grease to the shaft. Then either reinstall the prop or protect the shaft by wrapping it with cloth and securing the cloth with masking tape.

4. Buff the unit dry with a clean cloth or paper towels; then wipe it down with oil, or spray it with moisture inhibitor such as CRC.

Regardless of propulsion type, while your boat's ashore, pull the propeller, keeping the shaft key with the wheel. Inspect the prop carefully. If you find any nicks, dents, or other imperfections on the blades, by all means take the wheel to a good propeller shop and have it refurbished. A qualified prop shop can work wonders on a badly damaged propeller, returning it to new condition while restoring its original propulsive efficiency.

Remember to send the wheel to the shop in fall or early winter when the mechanics are not too busy. Don't put off until spring when you're ready to launch. That's the time the shop will be up to its ears in work, and you may have to delay the launching waiting for your wheel.

On the gasoline or diesel inboard auxiliary, take all tension off V-belts. Hanging slack, the belts will not develop hard spots where they contact the pulleys. In addition, pressure will be relieved from the bearings which carry the pulleys. Winter-long pressure on a bearing sometimes generates a tiny flat in the bearing race, causing the bearing to grumble or growl when restored to service.

If your boat is equipped with an outboard auxiliary, definitely remove the motor from the boat. Take it home and store it in your garage or cellar. Alternatively, trundle it off to an outboard shop and board it for the winter.

Secure from the elements, the outboard's power head can be treated to pretty much the same winterizing performance as the inboard gasoline machine plus attention to the lower unit.

1. Drain the lower unit, then refill with fresh lube (See Chapter IX for details.)

2. Remove the prop, sending it to the shop if need be.

3. Using a garden hose and an attachment specifically manufactured for the job, flush the engine with lots of clean potable water. The proper attachment is sold in outboard stores.

4. Drain all gasoline from the carburetor. With ignition off, squirt some clean engine oil into the carburetor air intake as you crank the engine by hand.

5. Remove the spark plugs. Squirt a shot glass of clean oil into the plug holes. Crank the engine a dozen times by hand. Replace the plugs.

6. Spray the entire unit with a mist of moisture inhibitor or wipe it down with an oily cloth.

7. Throw a loose tarp over the top. Don't wrap the outboard in plastic sheet. This material can't breathe. Sometimes it sweats, and the resulting moisture may harm the rig. Canvas is OK as a cover; the rougher the weave, the better.

If your boat is in wet storage, and you plan to visit her occasionally, you can leave the storage batteries on board, provided you have a means of charging them perhaps once a month. If you allow the batteries to go dead through simple shelf life, they'll suffer in two ways: Depleted cells sometimes sulphate, chemically deteriorate, refusing to take a full charge at a later date. Dead cells also freeze when temperatures drop to the frostbiting level. And alack, once frozen, they are dead forever and ever.

If you leave the batteries aboard, disconnect the positive cable, wipe the top of the case clean and dry; spray it with a mist of CRC. About once a month, hook up to the battery and charge it. You can measure when it is fully charged, using a hydrometer. However, avoid leaving the cells on a constant trickle charge, a charge of very small value. "Constant trickle charging is bad for the battery's insides," say engineers with experience in these matters. (See Chapter XI for details.)

Storing the batteries off the boat is a good idea. Either take them home, keeping them in your garage or cellar, or board them in the battery shop of a respectable boatyard. In either event, clean and dry the case, add mineral-free water to top up the cells, then make sure the cells are maintained at a decent level of charge for the entire lay-up period.

Unfortunately, the diesel or gasoline inboard engine is forced to remain aboard the damp, cold boat all during the long layup season. But, like the outboard auxiliary, some of its electrical equipment can be removed to drier places. Off-season marine environment is tough on engine electrical components, making it worthwhile, if you're inclined, to remove some electricals from the boat.

Items which you might consider taking off the yacht and placing in snug indoor storage are the alternator or generator, ignition coil, voltage regulator, and distributor. As you remove each component, carefully tag every disconnected wire so you'll know exactly how to reconnect them in their respective circuits. Be particularly careful with the distributor. Don't transfer it to dry quarters unless you are willing to suffer the trouble of re-timing it to the engine when recommissioning. However, if you do take the distributor home, you can lubricate it, install new condenser and points, and set the point clearance, all in the comfort of your own kitchen table or home workbench.

You must protect the engine against freezing, whether it's diesel or gasoline. Two possible approaches are:

1. Drain it, getting it as dry as possible.
2. Dilute undrainable water with antifreeze.

Open all drains, petcocks and plugs. When the water starts to dribble, probe and prod the passages with a length of stiff wire, loosening rust, dirt and silt, while allowing every possible drop of water to drain. Using lung power or a portable paint sprayer compressor, blow into all openings and drains. You want to get the inside of that engine as dry as possible.

Disconnect all cooling system hoses, letting more water dribble from the engine block. Dump residual water from the hoses, but don't reconnect them until it's time to recommission.

Suppose the boat is in wet storage? How can you disconnect and dehydrate hoses below the water line? And what do you do if she uses a "wet" muffler?

Shut off the seacocks. Disconnect the hoses from the engine, draining the engine as described. Now you've water remaining in the hose. Disconnect the hose at the cock, empty it, and re-connect it. If you want to purge the seacock, or if for some reason you can't unfasten the hose from the cock, do this: Blow into the hose as if you were playing a tuba. While blowing, open the seacock. You'll immediately hear a burbling and gurgling under the hull as air flows through the fitting. While the gurgling continues, shut off the seacock. Now, on its inboard sector, the fitting will be purged, and so will the hose. Leave the hose attached, and pour in a little antifreeze. This will completely protect the assembly.

Rather than leave hoses disconnected from seacocks on a wet-stored boat, proceed as described in the previous paragraph, then secure the hose in a vertical position so its upper open end is above the waterline. Cork it if you like. Now you have double assurance that if the through-hull fitting leaks, the boat won't founder.

Virtually all diesels and some gasoline auxiliaries are fresh water cooled, having the closed recirculating system described earlier. If your engine is this type, drain the coolant and, if you like, give it a flush with clean potable water. Close off the drains; fill the system with two parts of water to one part of permanent type antifreeze such as Prestone II, then run the engine for five minutes or so to mix the solution uniformly.

Suppose the boat is dry stored and you cannot run the engine? In that case pre-mix the water and glycol antifreeze before pouring it into the engine.

It's a good idea to put permanent antifreeze in raw water cooled engines. Not only does the solution prevent pockets of residual water from freezing, but also helps inhibit rust and corrosion. Should you choose this route, rather than leaving the engine dry, close off the drain cocks, then pour glycol-water solution into the system. Sometimes it requires ingenuity to work the solution in, but it can usually be done. Many auxiliary engines have a thermostat fitting on top of the cylinder head. This can be removed, and antifreeze poured in.

The sailboat is a creature of the water, happy and at ease when cradled in the brine. When she's hauled, she's ill at ease, stressed and uncomfortable; as a result, her hull distorts, changing shape appreciably. This is true of fiberglass yachts as well as those of wood.

Because the hull changes shape during dry storage, the relationship between propeller shaft and engine assembly becomes strained, the shaft trying to assume one alignment, the engine assembly another. Result of the forced misalignment can be heavy stress on the transmission to which the shaft is connected. To prevent stress, disconnect the shaft from the transmission. This is not difficult. Loosen the nuts and bolts or machine screws which fasten the shaft and transmission together. Remove the fastenings; then pry the two flanges apart a fraction of an inch. Now, engine and shaft are free to assume any angle they desire without twisting themselves or the hull out of shape.

While you're in the vicinity of the transmission, unscrew the plug, pull the dipstick, and inspect the gearbox lube. If the fluid appears pure and free of water, simply add additional oil as required to top up. But if the oil appears as though it may be emulisfied with water, drain or pump out the assembly and refill with the recommended lube. Most gearboxes require automatic transmission fluid; but before you pour anything into the transmission, read the owner's manual or ask a dealer to specify the correct oil.

Remember this when pottering about with the transmission: Some transmissions, particularly those with reduction gears, are water cooled. If your boat is stored where there's danger of frost, be sure the transmission's water jacket is drained. Also make sure that the transmission oil cooler is drained. This is a water-to-oil heat exchanger, usually connected by hoses to the engine's cooling pump and the transmission's lubrication system. Disconnect the water hoses, then blow all aqua from the exchanger so it doesn't freeze and split open.

Some sailboat exhaust systems have low spots which can trap water. Should that water freeze, it may break a pipe, passage, hose, or muffler. Ferret out potential low areas, and drain them. In some installations this may include minor disassembly of the plumbing, usually comprising hoses and clamps. If your muffler is the wet type, carrying cooling water, be sure to drain it. Some mufflers incorporate drain plugs; others must be disconnected and dumped out.

After securing the exhaust system against frost, drive a cork, stopper, or wood plug into the transom opening. Doing so will prevent water from entering and undoing your work. A stopper is also security against seawater entering the bilge if your boat is stored in the water. Wet stored boats have been known to sink when a heavy, soggy snow pressed the hull so deep that water entered the exhaust pipe and flooded the bilge.

Final steps in putting the engine to bed include spraying the back of the instrument panel with a mist of CRC. Also, spray or wipe down the entire engine with rust inhibitor or light oil, then cover it with a loose-fitting canvas tarp. Don't use vinyl or other non-breathing plastic wrap for a cover. That makes the engine sweat and rust.

If you can work it into your winter schedule, try to visit the lonely girl and see how she's faring. Lift the tarp and peek; see how the engineering department is doing; perhaps give the rig a wipe down or spray of rust preventer.

Another good idea, while you're visiting, is to crank the engine over a few turns by hand. Doing so will change the relative positions of internal parts, discouraging certain ones from taking a "set." As one sailor joked: "Mid-winter rotation of the engine distributes the rust more evenly."

XVII

Recommissioning the Auxiliary

Spring is traditionally fitting-out time. That wonderful time of the year we break out the sails, oil the winches, check the spars and tune the rigging. The air is charged with anticipation as the hustle and bustle of the boatyard, the smell of anti-foul, and the rattle of workmen's tools convey the feeling of good things to come.

Fitting out is fun. Sailors enjoy puttering with their boats almost as much as using them. Part of the puttering at recommissioning time should include getting the engine ready for the season. It's the old stitch in time bit: If you get the iron breeze off to a good start, she's going to reward your attentions by behaving more reliably during the season. Possibly she'll even prove that Murphy's Law is not absolute. She'll continue running just when you need her most desperately.

Arm yourself with a kit of hand tools, pad and pencil, replacement parts as required, and perhaps something to warm the inner man. Then spend an enjoyable day getting your mechanical second wind in good shape for the season.

Open wide the engine compartment and uncover the engine (it should have been covered for the winter.) Look it over carefully, and, using your pad and pencil, jot down the nomenclature of any parts which need renewing. These, you can bring to the boat during your next visit.

Inspect the exhaust system all the way from engine to transom, or to wherever the pipe terminates. (For additional details see Chapter XIV.) Most systems include considerable runs of rubber composition hose; examine it carefully, making sure the material is fresh and resilient. You may need a flashlight or drop light to see clearly under the decks, but don't neglect the job, because if an exhaust hose throws in the towel while you're offshore, you're going to have a disaster. Water spewing from the hose may flood the bilge to an alarming depth before you discover what's cooking.

If you uncover hose which appears old and tired, replace it without debate. Purchase hose which is manufactured specifically for exhaust use. Install it neatly, supporting it as required for a workmanlike job. *Double clamp* each connection: Use two clamps, not one, and use top quality clamps of stainless steel with a stainless steel screw. (Some clamps have a stainless band, but the tightening screw is carbon steel which rusts. These are lousy.)

After your yacht has been returned to service and has a few hours on her engine, crawl in with the engine and tighten the clamps again. Then you'll be set for the rest of the season.

If there's a plug or stopper in the exhaust pipe, pull it out before firing up the engine. Naturally.

Again using a flashlight if necessary, inspect the muffler and the piping connections made to it. Assure yourself that the muffler is secure. If it's one of those iron or steel monsters, watch for rusted spots and leaks. If you have to replace the muffler, consider a stainless steel model; they're lighter and neater, and are described in Chapter XIV.

Inspect all cooling water hoses, looking them over with a jaundiced eye. Unless each hose appears in new condition, fresh and resilient, free of cracks and checking, throw it away and install a new length of high quality hose. After slipping the new length in place, double clamp it with all-stainless steel clamps.

Safe, tight, efficient cooling water hoses are especially important on the sailboat auxiliary installation for this reason: The sailboat's engine is located low in the bilge, usually below the waterline. If a cooling water hose should rupture, seawater will flood uncontrolled, and, unless detected in time, will sink the boat. Therefore, it's not only important to engine well-being that the hoses are secure, it's also vital to the safety of the yacht.

Many diesel and some gasoline engines are fitted with a water trash and dirt trap that prevents silt, dirt, bits of paper, and other crud from entering the raw water system. If your engine is blessed

Fig. 1

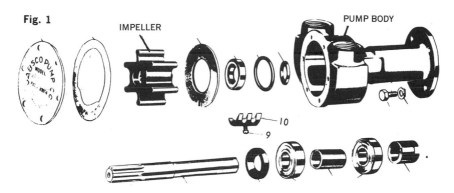

IMPELLER

PUMP BODY

Fig. 1 Exploded view of the popular Jabsco water pump. Good idea to renew the impeller at fitting-out time.

with such a trap, clean it.

Positive displacement water pumps using neoprene, rubber or other soft composition impellers are used on many diesel and gasoline engines. The Jabsco pump is typical. If your engine has this kind of pump, open it up (not a difficult job) remove the old impeller and install a fresh one. If you don't want to replace the used impeller, at least open the pump and rub some grease or oil on the metal surface against which the flexible vanes rub. If you don't nurse the pump a little, it may be badly abraded when you first fire up old Betsy. However, we do urge that you replace the impeller and lubricate the pump's insides. Doing so will almost guarantee that you'll have no pump trouble for the entire sailing season. A hint: Carry an extra impeller; it's a valuable spare to have aboard . . . just in case.

Most good seacocks have grease fittings. Taking a trusty grease gun in hand, force a bit of grease, preferably water pump type grease, into the seacock fitting. Work the handle, making sure the valve is operating freely. Leave all seacocks open so the engine can draw in cooling water.

When the engine was winterized, its drain plugs were removed or its drain cocks opened. Replace the plugs; close the drains.

If your engine is a diesel, very likely it has closed circuit cooling. See that the engine is topped up with a mixture of combination antifreeze and rust inhibitor. Some gasoline engines use closed circuit cooling, also. If yours is this variety, fill it with coolant.

Install fresh V-belts on the accessory drives. Some engines use one belt, some two. Don't be stingy; replace each belt on the auxiliary. Also, put a spare belt on board for each one on the engine. Belts are important. If one gives up the ghost while you're under power, the engine will overheat or its alternator will die, or both.

After installing a new belt, tension it firmly. Then, after the boat is afloat and has been operated under power an hour or two, retension the belt. A new V-belt stretches slightly, like a halyard, and also takes a "seat" in its pulleys. As a result it gets a little slack during the break-in period, and you must adjust it once again before it'll be happy for the balance of the season.

While you're pottering about with the V-belt which drives the alternator or generator, inspect that component's mounting hardware. The heavy bolt or bolts on which it pivots should be tight. Loose pivot bolts can generate all kinds of amazing noises. Believe it or not, loose mounting hardware can also cause electrical problems. All the generator's negative current, possibly many amperes, flows through the mounting bolts and bracket. Looseness there will cause high electrical resistance, leading to all kinds of mysterious problems in the charging circuit. What's more, sloppy mounts may allow the V-belt to subsequently slacken a mite: then you'll hear a screaming noise each time you accelerate the engine sharply. The scream is caused by momentary slipping of the belt.

Snoop around the alternator and voltage regulator, trying each electrical connection for tightness. Should you find any loose connections, remove the terminal from the screw or stud, clean both surfaces with fine sandpaper, then re-establish the connections, firming up on the fastening. Some alternator hardware carries a lot of amperage and the slightest electrical resistance in its connections will degrade charging circuit performance.

After making sure that the batteries are fully charged and topped up with water, bring them aboard and secure them in their battery boxes.

Suppose there is no battery box, the battery simply sitting loose in the bilge? What now?

Don't tolerate such thoughtless design. (We've seen it on a few boats.) Make, have made, or purchase a respectable battery box which will hold the battery secure against shifting, then, latch the battery in this enclosure and secure it in place.

Before attaching the battery cables, examine them, looking for broken insulation, frayed conductors, or corrosion. Replace any cable or ground strap which appears in less than new conditon. Ratty, acid-eaten cables cause more starting troubles than any other malfunctioning components except the old lead-box itself. Tremendous current flows through those cables, and even minor imperfections cause dire voltage drop, making the starter grunt rather than sing.

After you're satisfied that the cables are tip-top, use medium grit sandpaper and clean the battery posts. Again using sandpaper, clean and brighten both cable clamps. Now that all surfaces are rough but bright, firmly clamp the cables to the posts and you'll have a battery installation that's really done Bristol fashion.

But how about that battery? How old is it? What kind of performance did it render last season? Does it seem to hold its charge from week to week? If the unit is three seasons old or older, seriously consider replacing it. Experience shows that most lead-acid batteries are on borrowed time after three years. An exception might be made for top quality diesel starting batteries, but even here, age is against staying power just as, alas, in human endeavours.

Refurbish the diesel's air silencer and cleaner. Fitted to the engine air intake manifold, the accessory will choke off breathing air and reduce engine power unless kept clean. Similarly, remove and clean the gasoline engine's backfire trap or flame arrester which is mounted on the carburetor air inlet. Accumulated dirt and lint in the arrester will choke the engine, reduce power and increase gasoline consumption. Many an engine claimed to be "grossly mistuned" simply had a dirty silencer or arrester.

When the boat hibernated, the engine's crankcase oil should have been changed and a new oil filter element installed. However, sometimes this chore is neglected in the autumn. Pull the dipstick, inspect the oil. Do this after she's launched and the engine can be operated. If you look at the dipstick from an engine that has not been run for months, oil may look immaculate, yet there may be a stratum of contamination on the bottom of the crankcase. So run the engine; shut it down, then check the dipstick. If the oil is other than pristine, pump or drain it out; then refill the crankcase with a fresh charge. And don't forget to install a new oil filter element.

Pull the dipstick and measure the level of transmission fluid. Top it up if required.

Replace the filter elements on the diesel's fuel system. This is terribly important because if you don't do another single thing to keep your diesel operating smoothly and reliably, you *must* make sure that its injectors see nothing but pure fuel oil. The diesel is a tough customer; wet ignition can't stop it; a sick carburetor is unknown to it; but it has one Achilles' heel: If water or dirt reach its injectors, it dies.

Moral: Change those fuel filters.

As for the gasoline auxiliary, do the same. Change the filter or replace its element. Drain traces of water from the trap, then reassemble with the greatest of care, using a fresh gasket. After starting the engine, watch for fuel leaks. You don't want liquid dynamite dripping into the bilge.

If your diesel is fitted with glow plugs, see that they are screwed in tightly. If possible, use a torque wrench and snug them to the recommended tightness. Should a glow plug leak, even the tiniest bit, performance in its cylinder will be destroyed. Clean and tighten the electrical connections to the glow plugs. Unlike spark plugs, the glows operate on low voltage high current electricity and depend upon good connections for adequate performance.

While working on the head of the diesel, turn your attention to the injectors. Make sure they are tightened down securely. Test the fastenings holding them.

Spark plugs in the gasoline auxiliary: replace them. Don't rationalize that they may be good enough for another season. A set of plugs costs less than one small sheet block; so replace the set in your auxiliary. Adjust the gaps before screwing the new ones into place, then attach the high voltage wires securely.

How about those high voltage wires running from distributor to plugs and from ignition coil to distributor? Do they look fresh and resilient? If not, replace them. Nothing helps sure, fast starts on damp mornings more than fresh ignition wiring.

The distributor cap and rotor: Even if they look reasonably

healthy, fitting-out season is the time to replace them. As we learned in earlier chapters, the slightest defect in these components will ruin engine performance, especially in damp weather. Consider also replacing the ignition points and condenser. See Chapter VI for details.

You may need a flashlight for this next operation; it's an important one and shouldn't be neglected: Comb over that fuel system, assuring yourself of its safety and security. This chore is important if the auxiliary is diesel; it's life and death if the machine is gasoline. Your suggested spring security check might include the following:

1. Examine the manner in which the fuel tank or tanks are fastened to the hull. They must be tight and secure beyond any reasonable doubt. Tanks must not move or shift when the boat is heeled on her beam ends or when she pitches and pounds. You must, perforce, make sure that the tankage is secure and that there is no evidence of heavy rusting which might lead to pinhole leaks.

2. Assure yourself that the fuel fill is tight to both the tank and deck plate. If it is flexible fuel hose, double clamp it. Make sure that the fuel fill deck plate is electrically grounded to the tank. You might want to test this with a simple ohmmeter or low voltage test light. It's important. What's more, the fuel tank should be electrically grounded to the boat's bonding system. If checking on all this is beyond your abilities, and if you've doubts about the situation, you might want pay a marine surveyor to examine the components and their arrangements.

3. The fuel tank vent must spill overboard, not allowing vapors or spillage to enter the boat inside any combing or into the cockpit. Watch for this. If the vent includes a section of flexible neoprene hose, terminating at a metal fitting, the fitting must be grounded to the tank with an electrical jumper.

4. The line carrying fuel from tank to engine must enter the tank at the top, not the side or bottom. This safety rule is violated on many older boats, built by men who should have known better. If you find this situation on your boat, you might want to have the system reworked.

5. Look for drains or petcocks on the tank. If you find any, have them properly plugged. They're a dangerous source of leaks.

6. See that the fuel lines are secure and well supported. Don't

tolerate sections of dangling tubing.

7. Watch for a section of high quality flexible fuel line between the engine bed or frames and the engine proper. There should be such a flexible section to accomodate vibration and slight relative motion between the engine and hull. It is especially important that rubber-mounted engines be fitted with the resilient section.

8. Examine the engine for fuel leaks. If you find any, have them corrected. Don't live dangerously.

When you're satisfied the fuel system is secure, try worming your way behind the instrument panel. Snug up any loose electrical connections; then spray the back of the panel with corrosion inhibitor. Doing so will help prevent your electrical instruments from reporting false alarms in foul weather, possibly inducing you to abort a cruise unnecessarily.

Lubricate the controls, then test each as follows: Advance the throttle all the way. Then, turning your attention to the engine, see that the governor control lever on the diesel is positioned for full bore. On the gasoline engine, observe that the throttle is wide open. Next, close the throttle. Again looking at the engine, be sure the speed controls are closed to their respective stops.

Should the speed control, whether for gasoline or diesel, strike against its stop at the helm end before hitting its stops on the engine, repeatability of control will be erratic. Sometimes when you return the manual lever to the closed position, the engine will idle at one speed; at other times it will idle slower or faster.

Don't let a misadjusted clutch control make you a dock walloper. That's just what a sloppy control can do. Approaching a pier under power, when you throw her into reverse, *reverse* is what you want, promptly. If the clutch control on your yacht is manual, test it, making sure it has excess travel sufficient to move the transmission lever to its extreme positions and with motion to spare.

Should your auxiliary engine have a hydraulically shifted transmission, the usual connection between manual lever in the cockpit and transmission is a flexible cable such as made by Morse or Teleflex. On the transmission, the cable attaches to a lever measuring only a few inches in length. In order to positively shift the transmission, the cable must forcefully move the lever throughout its arc of travel. The lever has detents giving it a positive "feel" when it is in forward, neutral, or reverse.

When testing the controls, make sure that the clutch control cable definitely engages the clutch lever into its three positions. And the cable must have travel to spare. Have an assistant move the helm control to each of its three positions. At the transmission end, you watch, making sure that the control functions properly. If it has excess travel in reverse, say, but not quite enough in forward, adjust as required, using the clevis adjuster on the transmission end of the cable. Adjust so that there is equal excess cable motion both forward and reverse. (See Chapter XV for more information on transmissions.)

Before launching, install the propeller. There's a right and wrong way to install a marine wheel on a tapered shaft. Do the job the kosher way, delineated herewith:

1. Scrupulously clean both propeller bore and shaft taper.

2. Remove the key from the keyway and clean both.

3. Using a fine file or fine emery cloth, remove all burrs or chips from the key. Very slightly chamfer its edges. Try fitting it in the shaft keyway and in the propeller hub. The key must be an easy slide fit in both keyways; it must not stick or bind. Technically, it should have side clearance of about a thousandth of an inch; but don't worry about the hair-splitting.

4. Wipe the taper and hub with the very slightest smidge of light oil.

5. Do *not* place the key in either keyway. Position the prop on the shaft taper, press it in place and rotate it a couple of times, making sure it sits snug on the shaft.

6. Align the shaft and hub keyways; then insert the key. Do this while the prop is in place on the taper. Do *not* force the key in so hard that it upsets the prop. If the key is excessively long, remove it and shorten it on a grindwheel. When you tighten the nut on the shaft, the nut must not push against the key.

7. Thread the nut on the shaft. Tighten it. Put on the safety nut, if there is one, and insert the cotter key. You've done the job Bristol fashion.

The reason for all the meticulousness in installing the wheel is that it must make contact with the shaft over the complete area of taper. It must never be forced up or cocked out of track by the key. If cocked, it may seem tight when you launch, but will soon loosen and start to rock. Then you'll hear strange rattles and thumps down below, sounds hard to identify, albeit annoying.

There's one job you cannot do properly until after the boat is launched and has been afloat for several days. That is the operation of aligning the propeller shaft and engine assembly. We pointed out in the previous chapter that when a yacht is chocked up on land, it will inevitably hog or distort a little because even the best land cradle supports the hull less comfortably than water. For this reason, the shaft should have been disconnected from the transmission when the boat was hauled. Regardless, the two components should be realigned after the boat is afloat a few days.

Remove the bolts or machine screws which fasten the propeller flange to that on the transmission. (This may have been done when the boat was winterized.) Look at the two flanges when they are slightly separated. Their mating faces must be exactly parallel. Vertically and horizontally they must also align. If there's misalignment, you must shim the engine about in its bed until alignment is right on the money. Squiggling the engine about for a few degrees of alignment is not particularly difficult, particularly on engines with modern adjustable mounts. Don't be afraid to tackle the job. When the engine-transmission assembly and prop shaft are in nice alignment, replace the fastenings securing the two flanges, then snug up on the bolts.

The reasons for all the bother about alignment are these: with substantial misalignment, damaging pressures are thrown on the transmission bearings, and they may fail prematurely. Misalignment is also tough on the stuffing box, creating power-wasting friction, stressing the hull, generating thudding noises, and damaging the prop shaft.

When all's ready, start the engine and give the clunker a shakedown. When it's warm, adjust its idle speed. On the diesel this is an adjustment on the governor, and on the gasoline engine it is a screw which controls how much the throttle will close. Recommended idle speeds vary, but a nice idle usually falls between 700 and 900 rpm.

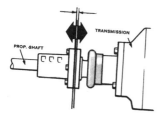
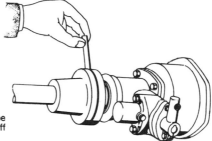

Fig. 2 Prop shaft and transmission flanges must be perfectly parallel. Feeler gauge or piece of stiff paper will help in "feeling" for a true match.

Avoid excessively slow idle because it invites the engine to stall at embarrassing moments, such as when you're maneuvering for a landing and the entire membership of the yacht club is watching—or so it seems.

Take her out under power. Watch oil pressure, cooling water flow, water temperature, and charge rate. Cast an eye down below at the stuffing box. While you're under way, the packing drips a little? Fine. Unless the dribble is enough to be of real concern, let it be; a few drops of water seeping through the stuffing cools the shaft, preventing excessive wear, heat build-up, and possible seizure.

That business about allowing the stuffing box to dribble a little sounds great. But suppose the dribble turns to a stream? Then you want to tighten up on the packing.

Loosen the set-nut. To do this, in most designs you hold the adjusting nut with one wrench and loosen the set nut with the other. If the metals appear green and corroded, a shot of penetrating oil will ease things up.

With set-nut loose, tighten up on the gland nut, the one which presses in on the packing. Tighten it a little; if feasible, just use your hands, not a wrench. Tighten *just* sufficient to eliminate the dribble, then pull up on the set nut so the adjustment will stay put.

If no amount of tightening eliminates the leak, the shaft is probably scored and chewed. In that event, you'll probably have to replace the shaft.

If you will carry out most of the operations we have suggested in this chapter, renewing hoses, clamps and V-belts, inspecting wiring, doctoring the battery, checking out the fuel system, and so on, you'll have a flying start on a good, trouble-free season. You'll have to admit: many of the troubles you suffered through in past years were the result of neglect and inadequate fitting-out. This season, properly recommissioned, you'll be well ahead of the game. With more sailing, less swearing.

Addendum:

Tools, Spares and Supplies

Just as you carry tools, marlinspikes, needles, blocks, shackles and spare line for the boat's rig, so should you carry tools, spares and accessories for her auxiliary. Details vary from boat to boat, and with the kind of auxiliary. But in general, you should consider carrying something like the following kit in order to administer decently to the needs of your auxiliary.

Tools

The basic tool kit should include at least the following: A small hammer, grease gun, oil can, pair ordinary slip-joint pliers, several screwdrivers, adjustable open-end wrench, pair of locking grip (Vice-Grip) pliers, set of combination open-end and box wrenches in these sizes: 3/8", 7/16", 1/2", 9/16", 5/8", 11/16", 3/4", and 7/8". If the auxiliary is gasoline, a spark plug wrench should be included.

If you desire a more complete tool kit, it should include, in addition to the above: a 3/8" drive socket wrench set complete with a ratchet handle, pair of long-nose pliers, pair of diagonal wire cutters, a medium size pipe wrench, set of hexagonal set-screw wrenches or keys, set of feeler gauges. Items rounding out the most complete tool set include a flywheel puller for the outboard and a propeller puller for the inboard.

Spare Parts

The farther you venture from home port with your yacht, the more extensive should be the supply of spare parts carried below. And those parts should be well wrapped, oiled, and protected against the ravages of moisture. Among the parts which you should consider carrying aboard are:

Spark plugs for the gasoline engine
Injector for the diesel
Fuel filter elements
Lubricating oil filters
Cooling hose and good stainless steel clamps
Alternator and water pump V-belts (these are important)
Fuses
Ignition points, condenser, distributor cap, and coil for the gas engine
Water pump impeller
Propeller
Voltage regulator
Generator or alternator

Supplies

Your supplies should certainly include appropriate quarts of engine lubricating oil, transmission or lower unit lubricant, moisture inhibiting or rust preventive spray, grease, penetrating oil, clean cloths or paper towels, Permatex gasket compound.

A good junk box is indispensable. Just as ham radio operators "never throw anything away," and build all kinds of rigs from their junk boxes, so should you be a collector of odds and ends which will be useful in the pinches. Among the rare treasures found in an engine room trove might be: friction tape, Band-Aids, hairpins, cotter pins, clevis pins, wire, solder, crimp terminals, nuts, bolts, washers, copper tubing, rubber tubing, clamps, stoppers, a small mirror (for peering underneath remote parts), clothes pins, plumbing fittings, gasket material, gaskets, chalk (for marking timing pointers), stuffing box packing, a silk stocking (for straining liquids), electric switches, fuses, and bulbs.

Index

T

ACKNOWLEDGMENTS

The author and publisher wish to thank the following manufacturers and organizations who contributed photos, drawings and diagrams.

British Seagull Co.
Chrysler Marine Division
Evinrude Motors
ITT Jabsco Products
Johnson Outboards
Lehman Manufacturing Co.
Medalist Universal Motors
Mercury Marine
Outboard Marine Corp. (OMC)
Onan Division, Onan Corp.
Paragon Gears
Perkins Engine Inc.
United States Coast Guard
Volvo Penta of America
Warner Gear
J. H. Westerbeke Corp.